SCOTTISH
MYTHS & LEGENDS

For the two wee Parcies in my house,
who conspired to become involved at every stage.

The author would like to acknowledge
the invaluable help of
Anne Newman, Kelley Doak and Kate Brown,
who helped to make sense of it all, and bring it together.
Thanks also to Melanie Woollcombe
and Hilary Rouse for help on the other side.

First published in Great Britain by Brockhampton Press, a member of the Hodder Headline Group,
20 Bloomsbury Street, London WC1B 3QA.

Copyright © 1998 Brockhampton Press.

ISBN 1 86019 217 3

A copy of the CIP data is available from the British Library upon request.

Created and produced by Flame Tree Publishing, a part of The Foundry Creative Media Company Limited,
The Long House, Antrobus Road, Chiswick, London W4 5HY.

3624 1000292605

CONTENTS

INTRODUCTION

Look not thou on beauty's charming,
Sit thou still when kings are arming,
Taste not when the wine-cup glistens,
Speak not when the people listens,
Stop thine ear against the singer,
From the red gold keep thy finger;
Vacant heart and hand, and eye,
Easy live and quiet die.

FROM *THE BRIDE OF LAMMERMOOR,*
SIR WALTER SCOTT

IGH ON THE HILLS OF SCOTLAND, where the wind answers the cry of the restless seas, where the land dips and soars, and the trees whisper of days gone by, there is a peat fire. And round that fire, fables are spun, myths are embroidered and legends unravelled. The wood folk dart among the trees. Over that hill is a loch, but the monster is silent once more, awaiting the day when the village charms have been cast aside or forgotten. That grassy knoll houses fairies, to be sure, and now, the storytellers draw closer round the fire, for when night lays her cloak across the land, it comes alive.

And so it was that the rich tradition of Scottish myths and legends, folktales and stories was born and passed on. The teller might be a villager, or he may have come from afar, a traveller or a caird. The story is his own, or it has been drawn from centuries of tales, sewn together and embellished. The legend is local fare – modern, perhaps, or as old as the land upon which their fire is lit.

The mythology of Scotland is varied and dynamic, spilling over with creatures from another realm, with transformations and mysteries, with wisdom and heroic battles, with morality and trickery. The thread that links the heritage of myths and legends in Scotland lacks the continuity of the classical myths, but it is distinguished, nonetheless, by a profound capacity to entertain, to explain, to produce a philosophy for living.

Mythology is a dangerous term to use here, one which has

Opposite:
Fairytales and tales of magic and mystery serve the purpose of explaining the unknown; fables were created to explain the nature of the earth, man, animals, the stars or land.

grown increasingly to mean myth in the classical sense, a story about superhuman characters or an earlier age, which usually explains how natural phenomena and customs came into existence. The mythology of Scotland is much more disparate, often closer to being history or literature than character-led adventure. The myths of Scotland express ideas about origins of people and of places – about the world as a whole, and the world that surely must exist under and above us.

The word 'myth' comes from the ancient Greek for 'word', and therefore means anything that is spoken – a story or tale of any kind. It has grown, however, to embrace a large number of genres and stories – those which are based on historical or modern legend, those which have a didacticism that enhances its purpose; fairytales or tales of magic and mystery which serve the purpose of explaining the unknown; fables which were created to explain the nature of the earth, man, animals, the stars or the land; and then those stories which were written with a moral message, for children, or to prop up religious belief.

There is an intense and fundamental superstition which feeds the myths of Scotland, and which produces a kind of pagan religion by which people were forced to live. The stories and folktales of Scotland were as ingrained in everyday life as any later religious dogma. There is a structure to the beliefs, and that is what forms the basis of Scottish mythology which, although certainly less lavish and expansive than that of the Greeks and Romans, exists in a comprehensive form.

Scottish mythology was, until very recently, an almost entirely oral tradition, and it was, for this reason, constantly changing shape. There was no Homer in Scotland, so the minutiae of their legends, of their beliefs, were never transcribed, never given credence as a whole, never linked in a comprehensive document. Today, much of Scottish mythology is lost, as a result of a dwindling population of travellers, and the death of the age of the bard, the caird, the village storyteller. And, while some stories have continued to circulate, to become part of the unwritten legacy of the country, many have disappeared, or changed so fundamentally as to lose their initial spirit and purpose.

Opposite: The myths of Scotland express ideas about origins of people and of places – about the world as a whole, and that which must surely exist under and above us.

The two different types of storytelling traditions in Scotland are those in Gaelic and in Scots. The Gaelic tradition, which has its roots in the Highlands, is similar to Irish storytelling, although littered with references to the history, the landscape and the clan structure of Scotland. The Scots tradition was based in the Lowlands,

influenced by Gaelic storytelling, but is much more like that of the English, with less ornamentation and briefer texts.

The transcription of Scottish myths was an arduous process for while the theme, the basic motif or the moral remained the same, the setting and character, and often the events varied with every new village. Unfortunately, until this century, the transcription process failed to record intonation, gesture, pace and often atmosphere, so that the myths lack the individuality that was so dependent on the personality of the narrator.

In the ninth century, a monk of Bango called Nennius produced a compilation of tales and legends of Britain, which was entitled *Historia Brittonum*, or *History of the Britains*. A number of Scottish myths and legends made their way into his collection, and this is the first major attempt at a written record of the oral tradition. He also outlined the history of the Scots in his book, and it is this document in which legends and myths become indiscernible from known fact. Nennius himself said that he compiled the chronicle of Britain's history and arcane lore because he felt the oral transmission was insufficient for future transmission to later generations. And this was largely the case.

But since that time, there have been many chroniclers, and storytellers with a keen knowledge of myths and an overwhelming interest in maintaining the tradition. The myths that have been recorded are often embroidered, and interspersed with other myths and legends, and local, often modern fact, but the basic premise still exists in these myths and without these early attempts to give them posterity, the heritage of Scotland would be much weaker.

After the ninth century, the nature of myths and legends changed, for these were now based more on true events, chivalry, heroes and great adventure. Heroes of the Scottish independence took precedence at that time, and much of the earlier material was lost. Because stories were passed more easily across the country by this point, and there was a more conscious attempt to produce fiction that was enthralling and evocative, rather than simply a good story drawn from an old legend, there was a radical change in the mythological fabric.

After that, there were other additions to the lore of the country. Witches, for instance, began to appear around the eleventh century, inspired, it is said, by King James VI and I, who was a great believer. Sir Walter Scott and Robert Burns produced material in the eighteenth century that mimicked some legends, reproduced others, and then invented still more. The heroes were based on historical figures in the Middle Ages, many of which were borrowed from England and from Ireland, including the great Fionn MacChumail (anglicized to Finn McCool or Fingal). The tales were based on a number of men who really existed – their magnificent feats joined together to become the career of one single man. Other heroes were fictional, developed to ensure the Scots some supremacy in the ancient world.

In 1760, a Scottish schoolteacher, James Macpherson, produced a ream of translations of what he claimed were verses from Ossian, son of Fionn. There was enormous controversy about these poems, which many considered to be fakes, as the original Gaelic documents were never produced. Until this time, there had been many tales, songs and poems attributed to Ossian, which preserved the legends surrounding him, but there had never been enough material to give the adventures of this hero epic status. Many consider Macpherson's translations to be dull and uninspired. He wrote in *Temora*:

> *The blue waves of Erin roll in light.*
> *The mountains are covered with day.*
> *Trees shake their dusky heads in the breeze.*
> *Grey torrents pour their noisy streams.*
> *Two green hills, with aged oaks, surround the narrow plain.*
> *The blue course of a stream is there.*

But whatever fraud or deceit existed in this collection, it provided many later poets and authors with enormous inspiration, and gave Scotland a hero when few had been recorded.

In the nineteenth century, John Gregorson Campbell compiled one of the best-known collections of Gaelic folktales and legends, painstakingly transcribing the stories, and attributing them to their teller and his location. His collection included many atmospheric touches, among them striking pictures of the storytellers themselves, which brought a surge of new life to an art which was slowing expiring. He said, in one collection, 'I found them to be men with clear heads and wonderful memories, generally very poor and old, living in remote corners of remote islands and speaking only Gaelic.' Of one of these narrators, Donald MacPhie, from whom Campbell collected many of his tales, he wrote:

> *He had the manner of a practised narrator, and it is quite evident he is one; he*
> *chuckled at the interesting parts, and laid his withered finger on my knee as he*

gave out the terrible bits with due solemnity. A small boy in a kilt, with large round glittering eyes, was standing mute at his knee, gazing at his wrinkled face, and devouring every word. The boy's mother first boiled, then mashed, potatoes; and his father, a well grown man in tartan breeks, ate them. Ducks and ducklings, a cat and a kitten, some hens and a baby, all tumbled about on a clay floor together, and expressed their delight at the savoury prospect, each in his own fashion; and three wayfarers dropped in and listened for a spell, and passed their remarks till the ford was shallow. The light came streaming down the chimney, and through a single pane of glass, lighting up a tract in the blue mist of the peat smoke, and fell on the white hair and brown withered face of the old man, as he sat on a low stool with his feet to the fire; and the rest of the dwelling, with all its plenishing of boxes and box-beds, dishes and dresser, and gear of all sorts, faded away through shades of deepening brown, to the black darkness of the smoked roof and the 'peat corner'.

The main difference between tales which have been transcribed, and those which have been maintained in the oral tradition, is the use of repetition. In literature, such repetition is wearing, in performance, it is an effective device to engage an audience.

The stories were often peculiar to the region, and certain storytellers had a range of tales upon which they called. Neil Philip, in his *Penguin Book of Scottish Fairytales*, quotes Campbell:

Each branch of popular lore has its own special votaries, as branches of literature have amongst the learned; that one man is the peasant historian and tells of the battles of the clans; another, a walking peerage, who knows the descent of most of the families of Scotland, and all about his neighbours and their origins; others are romancers, and tell about the giants; others are moralists, and prefer the sagacious prose tales, which have a meaning, and might have a moral; a few know the history of the Fein, and are antiquarians. Many despise the whole as frivolities; they are practical moderns, and answer to practical men in other ranks of society.

Many cultures, including the Scottish cairds, believed that all tales have a moral, and were a key part of the education of children and young adults. Therefore, most families nurtured the art of telling stories, and legends, of relating memories in their own homes. Hero tales were entertaining, and they provided Scotland with an elaborate and romantic history.

Unlike the mythology of the Celts, which demands that a myth fulfil a certain purpose, and a legend be based upon specific criteria, Scottish mythology is a tapestry of interwoven fact, fiction, legend, myth, fable, folklore – peopled by ghosts, witches and other supernatural beings, royalty, talking animals, fairies and other immortals, heroes and labourers. There is a spareness of detail in the tales, and an

Opposite: Many cultures believed that all tales have a moral and were a key part of the education of children and young adults.

element of wonder in almost every story, which becomes a distinguishing feature of the culture, and the splendid powers of imagination it engenders.

The Scots have always been a fiery, vital people, and Scotland a place of mystery and enchantment, inspired, possibly, by the spectacularly dramatic landscape. According to the blend of fact and fiction that has become Scottish legend, the Scots were born in Greater Scythia. A banished noble was sent to Egypt, it was said, about the time of the Exodus, and he married the daughter of the Pharaoh, Scotta. When the Egyptian army was drowned in the Red Sea, in hot pursuit of the Israelites, Egypt was so weakened that this noble feared for the kingdom, which was left open to invasion by the Scythians. Using the name of his wife, he drew together friends and companions and began what would be a forty-two-year pilgrimage to Spain, travelling through the Mediterranean, and along Africa and Gibraltar. Here, the Scots, as they were now known, lived for many thousands of years, at last giving in to the marauders and savages of the country by leaving its shores for Ireland.

And it was from Ireland that the first Scots made their way to the country that now bears their name, maintaining their fierce reputation although their numbers were somewhat diminished. They settled at Argyll, then called Dalriada, and the Scots of Dalriada produced kings of their own and lived there independently for many years. When they were strong enough, they took on the Picts, who were finally displaced.

There are many variations on this story; many disbelieve that the Scots ever travelled from the Middle East. Some give them mixed Irish and Pictish parentage, others adhere to the belief that they were deported from Assyria as Israelites.

In reality, the Scots can be traced to Ireland, through archaeological findings, and various manuscripts which exist. During the Roman period, the Celtic Irish were called 'Scottis', and it was these Irishmen who raided Britain as the Roman Empire fell. They spread across Britain (this can be traced by various inscriptions which mark the course of their invasion), and finally, some 150 of these colonists settled in Argyll, in the late fifteenth century. The leaders of this group were the three sons of a chief called Erc, which was headed by Fergus.

It was this group which spawned the realm of Dalriada, the kings of which ruled from Dunadd, in the Kintyre peninsula. And although the spirit of the intrepid explorer remained, these settlers were not distinguished by any great military men. It was St Columba

Opposite:
Scottish legends are peopled by ghosts, witches and other supernatural beings; there is an element of wonder in almost every story.

who brought them notoriety, when he founded his monastery of Iona, which was responsible for the spread of Christianity among the Picts. Scotland became a state in 1320, with the Declaration of Arbroath, when Bruce became king of Scotland.

With St Columba came a host of legends which have become a fundamental part of Scotland's history and subsequently her image. Columba, for instance, was said to have travelled one day to see the Pictish King Bridei, the son of the Maelgwn of Gwynedd. The journey was long and arduous, and St Columba was forced to climb the Great Glen and travel across Loch Ness. Here, on the banks of the river that enters the loch at Fort Augustus, Columba asked one of his monks to swim across to collect a boat from the bank opposite. As he swam, the monk was pursued by a fierce monster, who spat and roared at the poor terrified monk. St Columba stepped in and ordered the monster not to harm him, and the monster disappeared. Until this day, although the monster does make an occasional appearance, he has never harmed anyone.

There are other, exquisitely detailed stories which punctuate the career of St Columba in Scotland. His monastery at Iona became hallowed ground, and sixty kings are buried here, Scottish, Irish and Norwegian, including the great MacBeth. This graveyard was dedicated to Columba's brother Oran, who died there voluntarily when it was decreed that someone must be sacrificed in order to consecrate the ground. Legend has been built around this event, for it is said that after twenty days of being buried, when a pit was dug over his grave, he spoke, saying:

Heaven is not what it is said to be;
Hell is not what it is said to be;
The saved are not forever happy;
The damned are not forever lost.

He was buried then for ever more. St Columba died in 597, but Iona had become the centre of Christianity in the north, and would remain so for centuries to come.

By the time Columba died, the Scots had begun their fight for power, which was finally resolved in the ninth century, when Kenneth MacAlpine, a Dalriadic king, created the Scottish realm. He claimed the throne of Pictland, saying that he was born with the blood of the Picts, and he destroyed the most powerful Picts during a banquet at Scone. He was also responsible for bringing the Stone of Destiny there. These places still have a mystique and an intrigue that reeks of legend and the myths built around them, and many places like them still exist in Scotland and her isles.

The minstrels of word are few and far between in Scotland, and while her tradition has now been transcribed, and fragments pieced together to form a coherent mythology, it has ceased to grow further. Scotland's storytelling heritage has lasted far longer than in the rest of Britain, and men and women still gathered round the fire in this century, knitting, mending, preparing ropes for fishing the next day. And the myths, folktales, legends and stories which were told time and again have produced a tapestry which refuses to be unwoven, marking forever the vibrant ideology and vivid imagination of its creators.

> *The way was long, the wind was cold,*
> *The Minstrel was infirm and old;*
> *His withered cheek, and tresses grey,*
> *Seemed to have known a better day;*
> *The harp, his sole remaining joy,*
> *Was carried by an orphan boy.*
> *The last of all the Bards was he,*
> *Who sung of Border chivalry;*
> *For, welladay! their date was fled,*
> *His tuneful brethren all were dead;*
> *And he, neglected and oppressed,*
> *Wished to be with them, and at rest.*

FROM *THE LAY OF THE LAST MINSTREL,*
SIR WALTER SCOTT

✻   ✻   ✻

AUTHOR'S NOTE

There are many myths and legends which have not been touched upon in this book, and many variations of those that have. The stories are drawn from many of the genres which define the mythology of the Scots, and the selection was largely decided by the individual flavour of the myths and folktales. There has been no distinction made between legends, myths and folktales, because they have become united over the years to form a comprehensive whole. A scholarly attempt to separate them would be beyond the scope of this book. Instead, you will find here a selection of evocative and enchanting, myths, stories, fables and legends, many of which are well known, others which have been adapted so many times as to become unrecognizable. But all of what follows has had a lasting impression on our culture. The stories are drawn from many original sources, including Macpherson's tales of Ossian, Campbell's four volumes of stories, and more recently, Neil Philip's *Scottish Folktales*, A J. Bruford and D.A. MacDonald's *Scottish Traditional Tales*, and Geoffrey Ashe's *Mythology of the British Isles*. The author would like to acknowledge their very real contribution to this work.

LEGENDS OF WITCHCRAFT

'Tis now the very witching time of the night,
When churchyards yawn and hell itself breathes out
Contagion to this world: now could I drink hot blood,
And do such bitter business as the day
Would quake to look on.

MACBETH, WILLIAM SHAKESPEARE

itchcraft conspired to manipulate the lives of men and women, across the lands of Scotland, and across the ages. The old woman in the village might have powers that not everyone could understand, and when something went wrong, when illness fell, someone had to be given blame for the misfortune. The witchlore of Scotland was spawned and accentuated under the reign of James VI and I, who had an overwhelming superstition of and belief in them. Ultimately, however, the belief in witches reflects a pagan fear of spirits and creatures of the unknown. Witches could cast spells that enchanted, calmed, killed and controlled, and for that they were dreaded and continually plotted against. All witches were eventually defeated, but until that time, it was only safe to keep charms against unusual knots, or black cats, or strange happenings on the sea, for who really knew their origin?

The Brownie

IN SCOTLAND THERE'S a creature that's not a witch, or a warlock, or even really a fairy. He's a brownie, and he's ugly so he's not often seen by mortal eyes. For brownies are small creatures, with great bulging eyes, and faces that are furred like the backside of a donkey. Their teeth are like battered stones, and when they smile they set fear in the hearts of all men. But a brownie is a helpful soul, and although they are not often wanted round about a house or a farm, they work a kind of magic, and help to clean and to tend the farm or run the mill, for just the price of a bowl of cream, and the odd bit of oatmeal.

There once was a brownie who lived round about a house on a farm in Wester Ross in Kintail. The house on the farm was empty, so the brownie had made himself a happy home there. In this same village, near the house on the farm, lived a young miller, who shared a house with his mother. Now his mother was a greedy woman, and she dabbled in magic of all sorts, not all of it white to be sure, and she had set her sights on the young lassie at the big house on the hill, to be the wife of her young miller son.

The lassie was pretty, and her nature was kind, but the young miller was already in love with another, a servant girl who went by the name of Katie. Now Katie was as fair as the morning sky, and her cheeks were flushed with roses. She was a bonnie lass, and she would work hard with her husband to tend a mill and to make him into something grand.

Now the young miller's mother would have nothing of it: 'Look, ye must marry this farmer's daughter, with a big farm and everything, and it would be yours because her father's getting on.'

But the miller was stubborn, and he cared only for Katie.

'I can't help it mother, I love Katie, and I am gonna marry her,' he said firmly, to which his mother replied, 'You're not gonna marry Katie, because Katie is gonna die.'

But the miller's will was stronger than his love for his mother, and he married Katie in secret and took her to live in a deserted house on a farm. Now there were stories told in those parts about the brownie who had made his home there, but the miller was a friendly sort, and not easily scared, and so he convinced young Katie that it would be safe and together they went to meet with the brownie. Katie was a fair lass, and she could see that an appearance did not make a man, and although the brownie frightened her, she could sense his good nature and agreed to live there.

Opposite: Katie slept then, and when she woke, her baby was cleaned and swaddled, and the roses returned to her cheeks once more.

They settled in happily, in the house on the farm, and the brownie was made a fine bed of straw and bracken, and fed all the best bit of oatmeal and cream. For that he tended their mill, and each day new sacks of grain were laid neatly against the mill walls. He interfered not at all in their lives, but they came to love his quiet presence, his charming ways. For he would slip down the chimney as they slept and lay things just right, so that when they woke, the wee house gleamed from every corner.

As is wont to happen, especially with those who are young and in love, the young lady of the house became heavy with child, and as she grew more and more tired, the brownie would work harder, until he spent many a day in the house of the miller and Katie. He became a friend to Katie, and she became accustomed to his horrible face, warmed by his quiet presence, his charming ways. And when the baby was due to come, it was the brownie who she called to fetch her husband the miller, and he scampered with glee down the path to the mill.

Now the miller too had grown fond of the brownie, but he was more traditional than wee Katie, and he felt that the presence of his mother was necessary for that bairn to be born. And so he left Katie with the brownie, who mopped her brow as she called out with pain, and who stroked her face with his own furred hand. But as soon as the footfall of the miller's mother was heard on the path, he leapt up the chimney and disappeared from the room. For brownies are magic beings themselves and they know the dangers of a witch, especially those who dabble in magic that is not all white.

The miller's mother was friendly and calm, and in her pain and distress, Katie could not help but trust her. She allowed her mother-in-law to braid her hair, and to set her back against pillows that were freshly stuffed. A tiny black kitten was set by her side to keep company with her and the new baby. Then, turning the lassie's bed towards the door, she bid her farewell and left.

Now Katie was soothed by the presence of the witch, but when she left the pains began again in earnest and she moaned and writhed for two whole days before the miller was forced to go for help. He went first to his mother, but she feigned an illness and said she could not come back with

Opposite: But the Brownie was gone, for Brownies often do that, just disappear, never to be seen again. They missed the wee man's quiet presence and his charming ways.

him. And so he returned to the farm where he found poor Katie sick with exhaustion and great pain.

'I'll go for the howdie woman,' he said, for the howdie woman delivered most of the babies in the village, having the gift for midwifery. But Katie would not hear of it, so frightened she had become.

'Don't leave me here,' she sobbed. 'Send the brownie.' And that thought stopped them short, for many folk were frightened to visit them at their home because of that same brownie, and they wondered now if the howdie woman would fear to come as well.

But Katie's pain was dragging her deeper into a dreadful state, and the roses had disappeared from her cheeks. There was no sight of the bairn and there was nothing for it but to call the brownie to help.

The brownie was only too glad to help, and in the cover of darkness, with a great cloak wrapped across his hideous face, he rode off across the hills to fetch the howdie woman. And she came at once, for her calling was stronger than her fear, and she sat herself behind the brownie and wrapped her arms about him for warmth and for safety. And she whispered in his ear as they rode, 'Katie will be well again, no doubt, but I hope I don't see that brownie. I am terrified of that brownie!'

But the brownie said, 'No, don't worry, I can assure you for certain that you'll not see anything worse than what you're cuddling now.' And he drove the howdie woman to the door of the house and made off with the horse, into the darkness.

The howdie woman had seen no birth like this, and for four more days she sat with Katie, who was expiring quickly now, torn by pains that wracked her thin frame, and struggling to keep sane as they plunged her into a burning hell with every contraction.

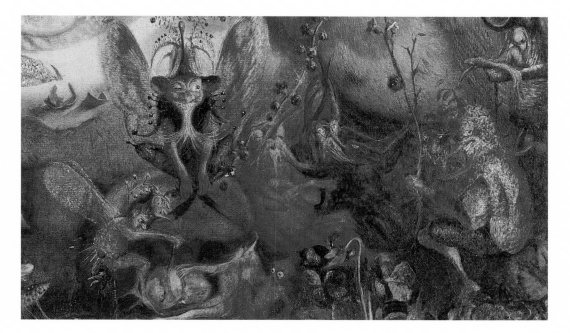

The miller sat brooding in a chair, helpless against this pain he could not understand, and suddenly he sat up and snapped his fingers. 'I'll bet a shilling,' he said then, 'that this is the work of my mother.'

So he rode straight to the house of his mother and shouted at her, 'Take that spell off my Katie. I know you've done something.'

And his mother shook her head, and said, 'I will not. I told you she is gonna die, and you are gonna marry the farmer's daughter.' She stood firm then and would not help his poor Katie.

So poor Katie seemed destined to die in agony, and he ran away then into the night, straight to the wee brownie, for he had no one else to whom he could turn. And the brownie thought for a while, and said, 'I'll tell you what you can do. Take me down to your mother.'

'Oh, no,' said the miller, 'that wouldn't help us at all. God himself couldn't help me against my mother.'

'Ah,' said the brownie, 'but you take me down because I can become invisible, and if you were to rush in and tell your mother, "Oh, mother, mother, you've got a beautiful grandson!" and then run off again, I will stay behind to see what happens. And I'll be invisible.'

And so it was decided that the brownie would come along, and when they reached the house of his mother, the miller ran in and cried, 'Mother, you have got a beautiful grandson.'

And she said, 'What?' her face a mask of alarm and fury.

'Oh yes,' shouted the miller, 'But I can't stop, I must see Katie.' And with that he ran back over the hills to wait for the brownie.

And as he went out the door, the woman stamped her feet and pulled at her hair, cursing all the time, 'Who told him about the witches' knots in Katie's hair? How did he know about the black cat? Who told him about the raven's feathers in those great white pillows? And who told them that I'd turned her feet to the door?'

And then the brownie skipped away, as fast as his legs would carry him, over the hills to greet the miller, and together they ran back to the house on the farm where Katie lay with the howdie woman.

Now the howdie woman had only to set eyes on the grinning brownie when she was up and out the door in a flash, but the brownie set himself to work, stroking the poor lass's cheek and mopping her brow, warming her with his quiet presence and his charming ways. He untied her head, and brushed it down around her shoulders, crooning softly in her ears. Then he took those great new pillows and set them aflame in the hearth until only dust remained of those evil black feathers. And then, with one angry twist, he took the head from the kitten and burnt her too, out of sight, of course, of poor Katie. And so it was, when the brownie moved the bed round, so that her feet faced the door no longer, that the cry of an infant was heard in that house on the farm. Katie slept then, and when she woke, her baby was cleaned and swaddled, and the roses returned to her cheeks once more.

But the brownie had gone, for brownies often do that, just disappear, never to be seen again. They missed the wee man's quiet presence and his charming ways, but he had milled enough grain for twenty odd years, and they lived on that house on the farm with their new baby in comfort and in good fortune.

The Three Knots

THERE ONCE WAS A FAMILY on the island of Heisker in Ulst. They were farm people and worked hard all the year, but when the harvest was over, and the grain tucked safely away for the frosty months ahead, they took it upon themselves to plan a little trip to Lewis, to visit some friends there.

It was the same every year, they crossed the sea and got to Lewis where they had a grand time of it, and then they went home again, to cosy themselves away for the long frosty months. And so it was this time, that they gathered an able crew and set off.

At Lewis things seemed much the same as they ever had. The man of the family went to greet the woman of the house they were visiting, and they talked for many hours, of days of old, and of good friends and family. And just as he made preparations to get off to bed, a tall lithe woman entered the room, with hair as black as a raven's back. Her eyes were cool and dark, and she whispered something to the woman of the house, and then she left, stopping only to stroke the woman's hair.

'Who's that ugly black thing,' asked the man, curious about the familiarity between the two women.

And the woman sighed and replied, 'Is that what you say? Ugly, is she? Woe betide you, man, but you'll be lost in love with her before you leave Lewis; if you can, of course.' And with that she rose and went off to bed.

Now the man scowled with the thought of it, for he had three great strong bairns and a lovely wife, as fair and pink and white as this thing was black. 'Indeed,' he muttered to himself, 'I won't fall in love with her.' He spat a bit of the old tobacco into the iron sink and prepared to retire himself.

Now he rose in the morning and the first thing that ate at his mind was the thought of that tall lithe girl, with hair as black as a raven's back, and he went downstairs, stormy as the North Sea waters. That night the girl came again to the house, though she'd not been out of his mind since her last visit, and he hated her even more, all tall and lithe and black, with those cool dark eyes. But when she left he longed for her like he'd longed for no other, and he grew black himself with rage and with desire.

Now this went on every day for a week, with the man from Heisker growing silent and cold, so his wife felt afraid and begged him to take leave of that house.

'We've had a good visit now, and it's time for us to be making for home,' she said firmly to her husband, and with the last tiny shred of rational thought left in his mind, which longed for the tall, lithe girl, with hair as black as a raven's back, he agreed.

And so it was that their belongings were packed, and their big strong boat made good, and they arrived at the sea to leave. But as the first foot was set inside that big boat, a great black gale was brewed and flung at them, and they could go no further. There was nothing for it but to return to the house from which they'd come, and to that tall, lithe woman.

And again the next morning they set out, but the mists drew around them then, cool and dark, and they could go no further. There was nothing for it but to return to the house from which they'd come, and to the cool dark eyes of that woman.

But as they walked away from the coast, they met a wee old witch, with hair that was whiter than the down of a thistle, and a small wrinkled face that spoke of great wisdom. And she stopped them there, and beckoned them aside.

'Well, my good folks,' she said, 'you've a bit of trouble leaving this dark place.'

They nodded, and listened intently.

'It's no wonder,' said the wee old witch, 'seeing the kind of place you've been staying. What will you give to me for fine weather to go tomorrow?'

Opposite: They were farm people and worked hard all the year. When the harvest was over, they took it upon themselves to plan a little trip to Lewis.

'Anything, anything we'll give to you,' said the wife earnestly, and looked to her husband, but his eyes were trained on the hill, on the house with the tall, lithe woman, with the cool dark eyes, and his face was rent by a longing such as she'd never seen before. 'We'll do anything,' she said again firmly.

'A pound of snuff,' said the old witch. 'And I'll need to have a word with the skipper. Send him by this evening.' And with that she showed them to the door.

So later that night the skipper of the big strong boat was sent to see the old witch, and there she handed him a rope with three big knots.

'Here you are,' she said. 'You take this aboard and you'll have a good day for sailing tomorrow. It'll not be long before you're at Lewis harbour. Now if you haven't enough wind, just open one of these knots. And then if that is not enough still, untie the second. But whatever you do, by God, don't untie the third.'

And so it happened that on that next morning, the day dawned clear and bright, with a fresh puff of wind to set them on their course. They loaded the boat, and without a backward glance, they headed to sea. And the man of the family let out a sigh of relief so long and frenzied that the others averted their eyes. His thoughts were once again pure, and the magic of that old witch had set him free. He called to the skipper.

'Untie a knot,' he said grandly, 'let's get us home at once.' And so a knot was untied, and a swift breeze blew up that sent them cutting through the waves.

'And again,' he cried, the wind cold on his body, his soul cleansed and clear. And another knot was untied, so that a great wind was let loose on the tiny ship, and they flew across the water now, the sails stretched to the limit.

And the man of the family settled himself on deck, and with the sea air licking his face, he felt safe from all danger, and perhaps a little too confident. For he called out then, 'Let's test that old woman's magic. What means that third knot?'

And his crew cowered away from him, and his wife shook her head, but he insisted, and being the man of the family, and in charge of his boat and his own fate, he had his way and the knot was untied.

What happened then is a story for the ears of the fearless only, for from the sea rose a sight that clamped shut the mouths of the men, and the wife and their children until their dying day. It was a shape, tall and lithe, with a face of sorts, from which shone cold dark eyes. And a hand was reached down, and the man of the family plucked from amongst them, and into the sea. And then the boat itself was lifted high above the waves, placed on the sands of Heisker from where she'd never move again.

Opposite: And another knot was untied so that a great wind was let loose on the ship, and they flew across the water now, their sails stretched to the limit.

She's still there, a warning to all who think that magic can be tested, and the land there has come to be called Port Eilein na Culaigh, or Port of the Island of the Boat.

The Daughter of Duart

THERE ONCE WAS A MAN, MacLean of Duart, who sent his daughter to become a scholar. Now in those days, an education was a novelty for a lassie, but so highly did he think of his daughter that he found the money, and sent her away. And a long time she was away, too, for it was three or four years before her feet touched the MacLean soil once more.

While she was gone, the man, MacLean of Duart, would sit himself in her room, and look around him. It was a fine room, it was, for so highly did he think of his daughter that he found the money to buy her everything she ever wanted. There were books a plenty, but since MacLean of Duart could not read, they meant nothing to them, with their drawings of cats, and circles, and great long poems. There were pictures, too, on the walls of that room, and a soft cover on the bed, that made it look just so. For she was a clever girl, and she knew how to make a room feel warm.

MacLean of Duart was lonely without his daughter, but he carried on working his land, and the day came again when she returned home to him there. And so it was that he took his daughter on his arm, and led her up into the hills, where the clouds quivered around them, and the air shone bright and blue. Then they looked around them, at all the beauty of the land, and he turned to her, his eyes alight with pride and joy, and he said to his daughter, 'How much have you learned?'

And his daughter stopped, and she looked about, across the mossy hills to the sea beyond, and there she pointed to a tall ship, which fought a course away from them against the waves.

'There,' she said, 'that ship. I have learned enough to bring it to shore.'

And her father laughed warmly, and taking her arm again, he said, 'Well, then, lass, bring her in.'

Opposite:
The prow of the ship drew nigh, and kept on coming until it was about to be wrecked on the rocks. 'Save them now,' said MacLean of Duart.

The ship turned then, and made its way across the waters towards them. And it kept on coming, as the water grew shallow and the sands rose up to meet it, and then the rocks were there, thrusting their way through the waves as the prow of the ship drew nigh. And that ship kept on coming until it was about to be wrecked on the rocks.

MacLean of Duart looked at his daughter then, and he said with a soft voice, 'Save them now, lass. Why don't you save them now.'

And his daughter shrugged her shoulders, and she smiled an easy smile, then said, 'But I can't. I don't know how to do that.'

There was silence then, filled by the crash of the ship upon the rocks. He turned to her then, did MacLean of Duart, and he laid down her arm. He looked at his daughter with new eyes, and he said to her, 'Well, then. If that is the education I have bought you, if that is what you have learned, then I would rather your room than your company.'

He strode home, and built a great fire. And when his daughter came in after him, he cut her to bits and burnt her there, saying, as he poked the flames, 'I will never have your sort in the same place as myself.'

And he went to her room, and gathered together her books, and her pictures, and threw them on the fire. Then he took her soft cover from her bed and put that on, too, till there was no trace of the girl who was his daughter. For MacLean of Duart thought so highly of his daughter that he could not allow her to practise the education she'd gathered, for he would have nothing to do with black magic, and she had mastered the art.

The Cauldron

THE LITTLE ISLAND OF SANDRAY juts firmly through the waves of the Atlantic Ocean, which spits and surges around it. No human lives there, although sheep graze calmly on the succulent green grass, freshened by the moist salt air, and kept company by the fairy folk who live in a verdant knoll. But once upon a time there were men and women on the island of Sandray, and one was a herder's wife, called Mairearad, who kept a tiny cottage on the northernmost tip.

She had in her possession a large copper cauldron, blackened with age and with use. One day, as she wiped it clean of the evening meal, she was visited by a Woman of Peace, a fairy woman who tiptoed quietly into the cottage and asked to take away the cauldron for a short time. Now this was an older fairy, with a nature that was gentle and kind, and she presented little danger to Mairearad. She had a wizened fairy face, and features as tiny as the markings of a butterfly, and she

Opposite: Then one day Mairearad had to leave her cottage for a day, to travel to Castlebay, across the sea on Barra. She was to go by ferry, as the dawn broke, and return by the light of the setting sun.

moved swiftly and silently, advising no one of her coming or going. Mairearad passed her the cauldron, and as the Woman of Peace retreated down the cottage path, towards the twin hills that marked the fairy's Land of Light, she said to the fairy,

> *A smith is able to make*
> *Cold iron hot with a coal;*
> *The due of the kettle is bones,*
> *And to bring it back again whole.*

And so it was that the cauldron was returned that evening, left quietly on the cottage doorstep, filled with juicy bones.

The Woman of Peace came again, later that day, and without saying a word, indicated the cauldron. And as days turned into years, an unspoken relationship developed between the two women, fairy and mortal. Mairearad would loan her cauldron, and in exchange she would have it filled with delicious bones. She never forgot to whisper, as the fairy drew out of sight,

> *A smith is able to make*
> *Cold iron hot with a coal;*
> *The due of the kettle is bones,*
> *And to bring it back again whole.*

Then one day, Mairearad had to leave her cottage for a day, to travel to Castlebay, across the sea on Barra.

She said to her husband before she left, 'When the Woman of Peace comes to the doorstep, you must let her take the cauldron, but do not forget to say to her what I always say.'

And so her husband worked his field, as he always did, and as he returned for his midday meal he met with a curious sight, for scurrying along the path in front of him was a wee woman, her face gnarled with age, her eyes bright and shrewd. Suddenly he felt an inexplicable fear, for most men have had fed to them as bairns the tales of fairies and the cruel tricks they play, their enchantments and their evil spells. He remembered them all now in a rush of tortuous thought, and pushed past the fairy woman to slam the cottage door. She knocked firmly, but he refused to answer, panting with terror on the other side of the door.

At last there was silence, and then, a weird howl echoed

Opposite:
Mairearad scolded her husband, and putting on her overcoat and boots, she left the cottage in the gleaming darkness, lantern in her hand.

around the cottage walls and there was a scrambling on the roof. Through the chimney was thrust the long brown arm of the fairy woman, and she reached straight down to the fire upon which the cauldron sat, and pulled it with a rush of air, through the cottage roof.

Mairearad's husband was still pressed against the door when she returned that evening, and she looked curiously at the empty hearth, remarking, 'The Woman of Peace always returns the cauldron before darkness falls.'

Then her husband hung his head in shame and told her how he'd barred the door, and when the fairy had taken the cauldron, he'd forgotten to ask for its return. Well Mairearad scolded her husband, and putting on her overcoat and boots, she left the cottage, lantern in hand.

Darkness can play tricks as devilish as those of the fairies themselves, and it was not long before the dancing shadows, and whispering trees sent a shiver along the spine of the fierce wife Mairearad, but still she pressed on, safe in the knowledge that the Woman of Peace was her friend. She reached the threshold of the Land of Light and saw on a fire, just inside the door, her cauldron, filled as usual with tender bones. And so she grabbed it, and half-fearing where she was, began to ran, exciting the attention of the black fairy dogs that slept beside an old man who guarded the entrance.

Up they jumped, and woke the old man, who cried out,

Silent woman, dumb woman,
Who has come to us from the Land of the Dead
Since you have not blessed the brugh –
Unleash Black and let go Fierce.

And he let the dogs free to chase the terrified woman right back to the door of her cottage, baying and howling, spitting with determination and hunger. As she ran she dropped the tasty bones, buying herself a moment or two's respite from the snarling dogs. For fairy dogs are faster than any dogs on earth, and will devour all human flesh that comes across their paths. Mairearad fled down the path, finally reaching her door and slamming it shut behind her. There she told her breathless story to her husband, and they held one another's ears against the painful wailing of the hounds. Finally there was silence.

Never again did the fairy Woman of Peace come to Mairearad's cottage, nor did she borrow the cauldron. Mairearad and her husband missed the succulent bones, but never again did they trouble the fairy folk. They are long dead now, buried on the grassy verge on the island of Sandray, where the sheep graze calmly on the succulent green grass, freshened by the moist salt air, kept company by the fairy folk who live in a verdant knoll.

✳   ✳   ✳

LEGENDS OF FAIRIES AND SEA-FOLK

The iron tongue of midnight hath told twelve;
Lovers, to bed; 'tis almost fairy time.

MIDSUMMER NIGHT'S DREAM,
WILLIAM SHAKESPEARE

hen darkness fell across the land, and the hush of evening brought sounds that belonged to no mortal man, the time was ripe for fairies and other wee folk to leave their realm and enter our own. Anything strange, complex or perhaps a little frightening must have a cause, and it was these creatures who were held responsible for acts for which no one else would take the blame. The mischievous deeds of the fairies and their compatriots were the cause of much illness and heartache, but by the same token, they could make a hero of a man, and bring roses to the face of a sickly baby. Fairies were dangerous, and folk from the sea could be fierce and unfamiliar, but the infinite battle to live with them provided a formula, a structure for daily existence, when life, and death and nature held all the fear of the unknown, and a crying baby, that tapping on the window, the light that glinted over the treetops meant something altogether different.

MacCodrum's Seal Wife

DEEP IN THE COLD SEA, long before men chanced the waves for the first time, there lived a king and his queen, and their lovely sea-children. The children were elegant, graceful creatures, with deep brown eyes and voices that filled the sea with laughter and song. They dwelt deep in that sea, in happiness and in comfort, and spent days chasing one another through the schools of fish, catching a ride on a tail, hiding in a murky cave, frolicking in the waves that caressed their young bodies and made them strong.

And so their days were spent, and they were fed and loved by the kindly queen and her husband, who brushed their hair, and stroked their heads, and gave them a home like none other. Until the sad day when the queen became ill and died, and left her children forlorn and lonely, but still with the sea as their home, and the fish, and the warm waves to comfort them. Their voices were softer now, and their music still sweet, but the king was concerned about their uncombed hair, and their unstroked heads, and he began to search for a mother for the sea-children.

The king found them a mother in a darker part of the sea, where the sun could not light the coral reefs, or dance upon the weeds and the shimmering scales of the fish. The mother was in fact a witch, and she charmed the king with a magic potion that put him under her spell. She came with him to the lighter part of the sea, where the sun kissed the elegant bodies of the sea-children, glowed in their soft brown eyes, and she made her home there, combing their hair, and stroking their heads, but never loving them, and so the friendly waters grew cold, and although the light continued to dance, and the waves lapped at their bodies, the children were sad and downcast.

And so it was that the witch decided to dispose of these sea-children, and from the depths of her wicked being she created a cruel spell that would rid the sea-children of their elegance and their beauty. She turned them to seals, who could live no longer in the marine palace of their father the king, their graceful limbs replaced by heavy bodies and sleek dark fur. They were to live in the sea for all but one day each year when they could find a secluded shore and transform, for just that day, into children once more.

But the witch could not rob the children of everything, and although their bodies were ungainly, and they were beautiful children no longer, they retained their soft brown eyes, and their music was as

Opposite:
They were to live in the sea for all but one day each year, when they could find a secluded shore and transform into children once more.

pure and mellifluous as the wind in the trees, as the birds who flew above the water.

Time went on, and the seals grew used to their shiny coats, and to the sea, where they played once again in the waves, and fished, and sang, but they loved too becoming children again, that one day each year, and it was when they had shed their coats, beautiful children once more, that they were seen for the first time by human eyes, those belonging to a fisherman who lived on an isolated rock, a man called Roderic MacCodrum, of the Clan Donald, in the Outer Hebrides.

On this fateful day he walked to the beach to rig his boat when he heard the sound of exquisite singing, and he hid himself behind some driftwood and watched the delightful dance of the sea-children, who waved arms that were no longer clumsy seal flippers, and who ran with legs that were long and lean. Their soft brown eyes were alight with happiness and never before had Roderic MacCodrum seen such a sight.

His eyes sparkled. He must have one. And so it was that Roderic MacCodrum stole one of the glistening pelts that lay cast to the side of the beach, and put it above the rafters in his barn, safe from the searching eyes of the young seal woman who came to call.

The seal woman was elegant and beautiful, her long hair hiding her comely nakedness. She implored him to return her coat to her, but he feigned concern and told her that he knew not where it was. In despair she sat down on his doorstep, her head in her hands, and it was then that he offered her a life on land, as his wife and lover. Because she had no seal skin like her brothers and sisters, and no place to go, she agreed, and so it was that the seal woman came to live with Roderic MacCodrum, where she lived happily, or so it was thought, and bore him many children.

But the seal woman, or Selkie as she came to be called, had a cold, lonely heart, and although she loved and nurtured her children, and grew to find a kind of peace with her husband, she longed for the waves, for the cold fresh waters of the sea. And she would sit on its shores and she would sing a song that was so haunting, so melancholy that the seals would come to her here and cease their frolicking to return her unhappy song, to sing with her of times gone by when the waves and the water comforted them and made them strong, when the sun in the lighter part of the sea kissed their elegant bodies and made them gleam with light.

And then at night she would return to her cottage, and light the peat in the hearth, and make a home for her family, all the while living her life in her dreams of the sea.

Opposite:
She would sit on the shores of the sea and she would sing a song that was so haunting, so melancholy, that the seals would come to hear her.

It was her unknowing child who found the beautiful fur coat, fallen from its hiding place in the rafters, where it had remained unseen for all those years, and she brought it to her mother whose eyes glowed with a warmth that none had seen before. Her mother kissed her then, and all her brothers and sisters, and whispered that they must look out for her, for she would be back.

Roderic MacCodrum of the Seals, as he had come to be known, returned to his cottage that night to find it empty and cold, like the heart of the seal woman he had married, and his children were lined on the beaches, bereft and alone, for their mother had left for the chill waters and she had not come back.

Their mother never came back, for she had gone with that lustrous fur coat, that gleamed in the light like her soft brown eyes when she saw it. They heard her, though, for from the sea came those same lilting melodies, happier now, to be sure. And they often saw a graceful seal, who came closer to shore than the others, and who seemed to beckon, and in whose presence they felt a strange comfort, a familiar warmth, especially when the sun caught those soft brown eyes they knew so well.

The Fairies and the Blacksmith

THERE ONCE WAS A BLACKSMITH by the name of Alasdair MacEachern, and he lived in a cottage on the Isle of Islay with his son Neil. They lived alone for the blacksmith's poor wife had breathed no more than once or twice when Neil was born to them, but Alasdair MacEachern, or Alasdair of the Strong Arm, as he came to be known, found great comfort in his son and they lived contentedly, with familiar habits and routines that brought them much happiness.

Neil was a slim youth, with unruly hair and eyes that shone with dreams. He was quiet, but easy, and his slight, pale frame gave him the countenance of one weaker than he was. When Neil was but a child the neighbours of Alasdair MacEachern had warned the blacksmith of the fairies who lived just over the knoll, the fairies who would find one so slight and dreamy a perfect prize for their Land of Light. And so it was that each night Alasdair MacEachern hung above the door to his cottage a branch of rowan, a charm against the fairies who might come to steal away his son.

They lived many years this way, until the day came when Alasdair MacEachern had to travel some distance, sleeping the night away from his cottage and his son. Before he left, he warned his son about the rowan branch, and Neil agreed to put it in its place above the door that night. Neil loved the green grass of the hills, and to breathe in the crisp, sunlit air of the banks of the streams that trickled through their land, but he loved more his life with his father and his work on the forge. He had no wish for a life of dancing and eternal merriment in the Land of Light.

And so it was that Neil wished his father a fond farewell, swept the cottage, tended to the goats and to the chickens, and made himself a feast of cornbread and oatcakes, and goat's cheese and milk, and took himself to the soft green grass of the hills, and walked there by the sunlit banks of the streams until dark fell upon him. And then Neil returned to his cottage next to the forge, and he swept the crumbs from his pockets, and tended to the goats and to the chickens, and laid himself in his tiny box-bed in the corner of the room, by the roaring hearth, and fell fast asleep. Not once had the thought of the branch of rowan crept across his sleepy mind.

It was late in the afternoon when Alasdair of the Strong Arm returned to his cottage, and he found the hearth quite cold, and the floor unswept, and the goats and the chickens untended. His son was there, for he answered his father's call, but there was no movement from his box-bed in the corner and Alasdair crossed the room with great concern.

'I am ill, Father,' said a small, weak voice, and there laid the body of Neil, yellowed and shrunk, hardly denting his meagre mattress.

'But how ... how could, in just one day ...' Alasdair stared with shock at his son, for he smelled old, of decay, and his skin was like charred paper, folded and crisp and creased. But it was his son, no doubt, for the shape and the face were the same. And Neil laid like this for days on end, changing little, but eating steadily, his appetite strange and fathomless. And it was because of this strange illness that Alasdair MacEachern paid a visit to a wiseman, who came at once to the bedside of Neil, for he was a boy well regarded by his neighbours.

The wiseman looked only once at Neil, and drew the unhappy blacksmith outside the cottage. He asked many questions and then he was quiet. When he finally spoke his words were measured, and his tone quite fearful. The blood of Alasdair MacEachern ran cold.

'This is not your son Neil,' said the man of knowledge. 'He has been carried off by the Little People and they have left a changeling in his place.'

'Alas, then, what can I do?' The great blacksmith was visibly trembling now, for Neil was as central to his life as the fiery heat of the forge itself. And then the wiseman spoke, and he told Alasdair MacEachern how to proceed.

'You must first be sure that is a changeling lying in the bed of Neil, and you must go back to the cottage and collect as many egg shells as you can, filling them with water and carrying them as if they weighed more than ten tons of iron and bricks. And then, arrange them round the side of the fire where the changeling can see you. His words will give him away.'

So Alasdair MacEachern gathered together the shells of twenty eggs and did as he was bidden, and soon a thin voice called out from his son's bed, 'In all of my eight hundred years I have never seen such a sight.' And with a hoot and a cackle, the changeling sank back into the bed.

Alasdair returned to the wiseman and confirmed what had taken place. The old man nodded his head.

'It is indeed a changeling and he must be disposed of, before you can bring back your son. You must follow these steps: light a large, hot fire in the centre of the cottage, where it can be easily seen by the changeling. And then, when he asks you "What's the use of that", you must grab him by the shirtfront, and thrust him deep into the fire. Then he'll fly through the roof of the cottage.'

Alasdair of the Strong Arm did as requested, certain now that that wizened, strange creature was not his son, and as the fire began to roar, the voice called out, reedy and slim, 'What's the use of that?' at which the brave blacksmith seized the body that lay in Neil's bed and placed it firmly in the flames. There was a terrible scream, and the changeling flew straight through the roof, a sour yellow smoke all that remained of him.

And so Alasdair MacEachern cleared away the traces of the fire, and returned once more to the man of knowledge, for it was time to find his son, and he could delay no longer.

The wiseman bade him go to fetch three things: a Bible, a sword, and a crowing cock. He was to follow the stream that trickled through their land to the grassy green knoll where the fairies danced and played eternally.

Opposite: The fairies began to dance, a slow and wiry gyration, moving to a weird song that tugged at the mind of the blacksmith and threatened to overcome him.

On the night of the next full moon, that hill would open, and it was through this door that Alasdair must go to seek his son.

It was many days before the moon had waned, and then waxed again, but it stood, a gleaming beacon in the sky at last, and Alasdair MacEachern collected together his sword and his Bible and

his crowing cock and set out for the green knoll where the fairies danced. And as the moon rose high in the sky, and lit the shadowy land, a door burst open in the hill, spilling out laughter and song and a bright light that blazed like the fire in the hearth of the blacksmith's cottage. And it was into that light and sound that the courageous Alasdair MacEachern stepped, firmly thrusting his sword into the frame of the door to stop it closing, for no fairy can touch the sword of a mortal man.

There, at a steaming forge, stood his son, as small and as wild-looking as the little folk themselves. He worked silently, absorbed in his labours, and started only when he heard the voice of his father.

'Release my son from this enchantment,' shouted Alasdair MacEachern, holding the Bible high in the air, for fairies have no power over mortals who hold the good Lord's book, and they stood back now, cross and foiled.

'Return him to me, to his own land,' bawled the blacksmith, but the fairies began to smirk, and they slowly crept around him in a circle, taunting him, poking at him with blades of honed green grass. They began to dance, a slow and wiry gyration, moving to a weird song that tugged at the mind of the blacksmith, that threatened to overcome him. He struggled to stay upright, and as he stabbed his arms out in front of him, he dropped his cock, who woke with a howl and gave one mighty crow that sent the little fairies shrieking from the doorway to the other side, sent them howling away from the cock and the blacksmith and his son, who they pushed now towards him, sending them all slipping towards the threshold of their world. For daylight was the curfew of the fairies, and it was with true fear that the crow of the red-combed cock was heard, for little people may never see the light of day per chance they turn at once to stone.

They struggled now, prodding the mortals from their world, and begging in an awkward chant for Alasdair MacEachern to release his dirk from their door. And as he drew it from the threshold, and stood once more in the land of mortals with his son, a small and crafty fairy thrust his face from the hillside, and called out a curse that fell upon the son of the hapless blacksmith like the mist of a foggy night.

'May your son not speak until the day he breaks the curse.' The head popped back, and the fairy was gone, never to be seen again.

And so it was that Alasdair MacEachern and his son Neil went to live again in their familiar, cosy cottage next to the forge, and took up their work, their habits and their routines in place once more. Neil's tongue was frozen by the curse of the fairies, but his manner was unchanged, and this father and his son lived contentedly, for speech is not always necessary to those who live simply, with things and people to which they have grown accustomed.

One day, a year and a week from the fairy's fateful full moon, Alasdair set his son the task of forging the new claymore for the Chief of his clan. As his silent son held the metal to the fire, he started, and looked for one instant as wild as he had in the Land of the Light, for suddenly Neil had remembered, and in that flash of memory he recalled the intricate forging of the fairies' swords, how he'd learned to temper the blades of their glowing weapons with words of wisdom and charms, with magic and spells as well as with fire. Now he leapt into action, and worked with a ferocity and speed that set his father, Alasdair of the Strong Arm, reeling with shock and with fear.

And then the motion stopped, and holding up a sword that gleamed like the light of the full moon, he said quietly, 'There is a sword that will never fail the man who grasps it by the hilt.'

From that time onwards Neil spoke again, for unwittingly he had removed the curse of the fairies by fashioning a fairy sword to sever a fairy spell. Never again did he remember his days in the fairy kingdom, never again could he forge a fairy sword, but the Chief of his clan never lost a battle from that day, and the sword remained the greatest of his possessions.

Neil and his father, Alasdair MacEachern, returned to their cottage, the finest blacksmiths in all the land, their forge casting a glow that could be seen from hills all round, almost as far as the Land of Light, where the fairies kick up their heels in fury at the thought of that blacksmith and his clever son.

The Fairy Changeling

THERE ONCE WAS A WOMAN who lived on the sea, where the winds blew cold and damp. By day she combed the sands for seaweed, and by night she lay alone in her bed, weak and lonely, for her husband was a fisherman and by the light of the moon he trawled the rocky coasts, eking a cruel living, but one which kept them fed and warm in a cosy cottage.

The woman longed for a child, but it was many years before she was granted her wish, and when her baby finally came he was small and feeble.

Her neighbours said he would die, or worse, be snatched by the fairies who loved a child so fair of complexion, so slight of build. He would be taken, they said, to the Land of Light where the fairies danced and sang and played all day, where they set traps and tricks for mortal folk who crossed their merry paths.

The fisherman's poor wife could not help but think that a life of laughter would bring roses to the cheeks of her white child, and she wished with all her being that he would be stolen by the fairies, and taken to a land where he could become strong. And so it was that the fisherman's wife set her child out on the rocks, on the edge of her land, and watched and waited. She slept for a few moments, but otherwise moved not, and still her baby lay there, swaddled and spiritless, an invitation to the little folk which was not accepted.

At length she berated herself for the foolhardy actions, and brought her baby into the cottage once more. And there he surprised her by pulling himself up and demanding food, attaching himself to her teat with such relish that she drew back. He suckled the woman dry, and then demanded porridge, but still he lay small and wizened, more yellow than before, but so hungry that she could not feed him.

So the fisherman's wife placed her baby at her breast, and went to see the wiseman in the village, anxious about her small but starving baby, frightened by his curious change.

The wiseman listened carefully to her story, silently shaking his head.

'You have not your own bairn, but a fairy changeling,' he said finally.

The wife of the fisherman balked, for there in front of her was the very shape and likeness of her baby, and the cry was as shrill as ever. She refused to believe him.

'Take him, then, to your cottage, and leave him in his cradle. Shut the door, but do not go. Spy upon him there and you will be sure.'

And so the fisherman's wife returned to her cottage, and laid the baby upon his bed, shutting the door firmly behind her, but skulking back to peer in the window. And suddenly her baby sat up and drew from under the mattress a chanter, which he began to play. And instead of her baby there was an old fairy bodach.

Opposite: By day she combed the sands for seaweed, huddling against the fevered winds which blew cold and damp.

She fairly flew back to the wiseman, and implored him to help her get rid of the changeling, sickened at the thought of having suckled that gnarled old creature. Calmly the wiseman told her what to do.

The very next day, the wife of the fisherman took her changeling baby and laid him on a rock by the sea, busying herself by collecting seaweed as she did on every day that passed, and comforted by this routine, the baby, or the fairy bodach as she now knew he was, fell asleep. As he slept the tide drew in, licking at the rock on which he slept, until the waters began to dampen his wrappings, and he woke with a start. When he realized that he could not reach the fisherman's wife without swimming he rose to his full height, and a little fairy man once more he began to stamp his feet and howl, shaking his fist at the fisherman's wife who stood entranced as the waters threatened to engulf the fierce fairy.

And so it was that ten or twelve small fairies appeared to rescue their kin, but since fairies cannot swim, they danced helplessly on the shore while the water grew higher and higher about the rock. The fisherman's wife was smug, and she said, 'I shall leave him there, until you return my baby.'

And the fairies disappeared and returned with her baby, who had grown in his time away from his mother, and whose cheeks were roses, whose white skin held the bloom of good health. And she thanked the fairies, and returned their bodach to them.

So the fisherman's wife, flushed with her good fortune, went back to her cosy cottage, protected from the winds which blew cold and damp

from the sea. She lived there with her blossoming baby, by day combing the sands for seaweed, and at night nestling warm in her bed with her son, silently thanking the little people who had made him strong.

The Thirsty Ploughman

IT WAS IN BERNERAY that two men from Brusda walked along a hot and sunburnt field, parched from the fiery sun, from a long day of ploughing. Sweat glistened on their brows and they talked little, saving words for a time when their tongues were moister. Their feet were bare and despite the great heat they moved quickly, thirsting for a drink, for cool refreshment.

They passed across a rocky knoll and then they heard a woman, working at a churn. They looked at one another with relief.

'Ah, Donald,' said Ewan, the slighter of the two men, 'if the milkmaid had my thirst, what a drink of buttermilk she would drink.'

Donald was not sure. 'Ah, it's not buttermilk I would care for,' he said.

As they carried on over the dry brush that lined the hillock, the sound of the fresh milk splashing in the churn grew louder, more enticing, and both men licked their lips at the thought of it. There before them stood a fair maiden, her apron starched crisp white, holding a jug that foamed with pure buttermilk. She offered it to them then, Ewan first because he was the smaller of the two.

Ewan refused to drink because he knew neither the maiden nor the source of the buttermilk. He was afraid of what he did not know and though he thirsted for the cool milk, he would allow none to pass his lips.

Donald, who cared not for buttermilk, drank deeply from the jug, and wiping the frosting of white lather from his lip, he declared it the best he had ever tasted.

'Ah,' said the bonny maiden, whose face was cool with contempt, 'you who asked for the drink and did not accept it will have a short life. And you,' she gestured to Donald, 'you who took the drink, but did not ask for it, a long life and good living.'

She turned on her heel, and apron bright in the sunlight, left the men, one thirsty and one sated.

And so it was that Ewan returned home that night and took to his bed, never to waken, for the fear of God had been put into him

Opposite:
The tide drew in, as it did every evening, and it licked at the rocks and the carefully combed sands. The baby was atop a rock, and soon he would be stranded by the churning waters.

that day by the maiden on the hill, who could be none other than a witch. And Donald lived a long and prosperous life, ploughing his field alone, but reaping better crops, and amassing great riches. He looked always across the knoll, listened intently for the sound of milk in the churn, but never again did he see the witch, or fairy, though he blessed her often.

Wee Johnnie in the Cradle

THERE ONCE WAS A man and his wife who lived on a farm on the edge of a wood where fairies were known to lay their small hats. They were a young man and wife and they had not been married long before a child was born to them, a child they called Johnnie. Now wee Johnnie was an unhappy baby, and from the beginning he cried so loudly that the birds ceased their flight over the farmer's cottage, and the creatures of the woodland kept a surly distance. The man's wife longed for the days when she could tend the fields with her husband, and chat to him of things which those who are newly wed have to chat of, and to go to market, where they would share a dram and have a carry-on like they had in the days before wee Johnnie was born.

But Johnnie was there now, and their cosy cottage became messy and damp, and some days the hearth was not lit because the man and his wife were so intent on silencing the squalling boy, and some days they could not even look one another in the eye, so unhappy and disillusioned they had become.

And then, perchance, a kindly neighbour, a tailor by trade, took pity on the man and his wife, who grew ever thinner and ever more hostile as the cries of wee Johnnie grew wilder and lustier as he grew larger and stronger.

'I'll take yer bairn and ye can take yer wife to market,' he said to the farmer one day, and the man and his wife eagerly agreed and set off for the day.

They had not been gone longer than a minute or two, when the kindly tailor, who had placed himself beside the fire and was bracing himself for an afternoon of wailing, was startled from his reverie by a deep voice.

'Fetch me a glass o' that whiskey, there, in the press,' it said. And the tailor looked about him in amazement, the room empty but for the wee Johnnie in the cradle who was mercifully silent.

Opposite:
And Donald lived a long and prosperous life ploughing the field alone, but reaping better crops and amassing great riches.

'I said to ye, fetch me a glass,' and up from the cradle of wee Johnnie popped wee Johnnie's head, and from the mouth on that head came that deep and bossy voice.

The tailor rose and did as he was bidden, and when the baby had drained the glass, and then another, and let out a belch that was very unbabyish indeed, he said to the wee bairn, 'You aren't Johnnie, are ye, ye are a fairy without a doubt.'

'And if I am,' said the fairy changeling, 'what will ye say to them, me mam and da?'

'I, I dunna know,' said the tailor carefully, settling himself back into his chair to watch the fairy more carefully.

'Get me some pipes,' said Johnnie the fairy, 'I like a bit of music with me drink.'

'I haven't any ... and I dunna play,' said the tailor, crossing himself and moving further from the loathsome baby.

'Fetch me a straw then,' he replied. And when the tailor complied, the fairy Johnnie played a song which was so exquisite, so effortlessly beautiful that the tailor was quite calmed. Never before had he heard music so haunting, and he would remember that melody until his dying day, although he could never repeat it himself or pass it on. But he was broken from his reverie, for wee Johnnie was speaking.

'Me mam and da, when will they be back?' he whispered.

The tailor looked startled, for the day had been pulled from under him, and it was time indeed for the farmer and his wife to return. He looked anxiously from the window and as they drew up he heard wee Johnnie begin to howl with all the vigour of a slaughtered beast, and he watched as a deep frown furrowed the brow of the farmer's wife, and a dull shadow cast itself across the face of her husband.

He must tell them, for the cruel fairy was manipulating them, taunting them with his tortuous cries. And their own wee bairn was somewhere lost to them.

He pulled the farmer aside as his wife went to tend to the wailing bairn, and told him of the fairy. A bemused look crossed his face and he struggled to keep his composure. 'My wife, she'll not believe it,' he said finally.

But the tailor had a plan. He told the farmer to pretend to leave for market the following day, and he, the tailor, would step in to look after the bairn once again. But the farmer and his wife were

Opposite:
They set off for the market and there they shared a dram and a carry-on like they had in the days before wee Johnnie was born.

not really to leave, they should hide themselves outside the cottage walls and watch when the wee Johnnie thought them gone.

And so it happened that the next day the man and his wife set out for market again, but drove their horses only round the grassy bend, returning stealthily to look through the windows of their cottage. And there was wee Johnnie, sipping on a glass of their best whiskey, puffing idly on a straw pipe that played a song which was so exquisite, so effortlessly beautiful that they were quite calmed. Never before had they heard music so haunting, and they would remember that melody until their dying day, although they could never repeat it.

But when they heard that wee Johnnie's coarse voice demanding more drink, they were snapped from their reverie, and they flew into the cottage and thrust the changeling intruder on the burning griddle which the tailor had prepared for that purpose.

And the scream that ensued was not that of their own baby, and the puff of sickening smoke which burst from the fairy as he disappeared renewed their determination.

And then there was silence, an empty peace that caused the man and his wife to look at one another in dismay, for what had they done to cause their baby to be stolen from them, and where was their own wee Johnnie now?

Then a gurgle burst forth, and there was a movement in the corner of the room where the tiny cradle lay. They rushed to its side, and there lay Johnnie, brought back from his fairy confinement, smiling and waving tiny fat arms, with cheeks like pink buttons, and a smile so merry that the cottage of the man and his wife was warmed once again.

The tailor left them then, a grin on his face as he whistled to himself a tune which was so exquisite, so effortlessly beautiful that he was quite calmed.

The Fairy Dancers

It was Christmas Eve and by the Loch Etive sat two farmers, longing for a drink but with an empty barrel between them. And so it was decided, on that icy Christmas Eve, that these two farmers would walk the road to Kingshouse, their nearest inn, and they would buy a barrel of the best whiskey there, a three-gallon jar that would warm them through the frosty months to come.

So they set off along the winding road, and over the hills that glistened with snow, all frosted with ice, and came to the warm wooded inn at Kingshouse. It was there that a cup of tea was shared, and a wee dram or two, and so the two men were quite merry as they set off home again, the three-gallon jar heavy on the back of the youngest man, for they would take turns carrying its weight on the long journey down the winding road and over the hills.

And over the hills they went but they were stopped there, by the need for a taste of that whiskey, and for a smoke. Then the sound of a fantastic reel grew louder and louder, and a light shone brighter over the hills, towards the north.

'Och, it's just a wee star,' said one man, ready for his smoke and his tipple.

'Nah, it's a light, and there's a party there to be sure,' said the other, who was a great dancer and loved a reel more than any other.

So they crossed the brae to the north, towards the light, and the sound of pipes, which played a fine tune. There in front of them were dancers, women in silk dresses, bowing and twirling, and men in highland dress, with pipes playing an enchanted, fine tune that drew them towards the hill.

The younger man, who carried the jar, went first, and as he entered the great door in the hillside, and joined the merry throng, the door was closed. When the other farmer, slower than the first, reached the site, there was nothing to be found. For his friend had disappeared and there was no trace of him.

It was a cold and lonely walk home, and the farmer puzzled over what had occurred on that moonlit hill, with a magical reel playing from a light that shone in the darkness. He went first to the farm of the other man, and he told his wife what had happened, but as he talked, faces closed, and brows became furrowed, and it was clear that he was not believed, that no man could lose his friend on a hill just a few miles from home.

And so it was that the policemen were called from Inveraray, and they took him away and asked him questions that made his head spin, and caused him to slump over in exhaustion, and he wished more than anything for a drop of the whiskey that was hung on the other man's back. They kept him there, the police, and he was sent to trial, but he told them all the same thing, how a magical reel had played from a light that shone in the darkness, and how his friend had disappeared without trace.

He was sent back to that prison, and when they asked him again, he could only tell the truth of that fateful night, so they asked him no more, and sent him home, for he would not budge from his story, and that story never changed.

And it was near twelve months before this man had cause to travel past that hill again, and with him this time were some lads from the village who had set themselves the task of catching some fish for the Christmas feast. And with a basket full of fish, they stopped on their way back to their homes, with the need for a smoke and a taste of the whiskey that the farmer had tucked in his belt. And there again they heard that fantastic music, and saw the light beaming from the darkness of the hills.

But the lads from the village had heard too much of this madness, and they struggled home with the fish, ahead of the farmer who wanted more than anything to find his friend, and that barrel of whiskey. So the farmer climbed over the hills, towards that light, and he heard there the sound of pipes, which played a fine tune. There in front of him were dancers, women in silk dresses, bowing and twirling, and men in highland dress, with pipes playing an enchanted, fine tune that drew him towards the hill.

And he stuck his fishing hook in the threshold of the door, for no fairy can touch the metal of a mortal man, and he entered the room which spun with the music, and threatened to drag him into its midst. But this farmer never liked a dance, preferring instead a good smoke and a dram of whiskey, and he resisted the calls on his soul, and struggled through the crowd to find his friend the farmer, who danced in the middle of the reel like a man possessed.

'Och, lad, we've only just begun,' the dancer protested, as his friend dragged him away.

And since he had danced for near twelve months with that barrel on his back, he carried it home again, along the winding road and over the hills that glistened with snow, all frosted with ice. They came to the farm of the man who'd been dancing, and what a surprise met his poor lonely wife when she opened the door. For there was her husband, just skin and bones to be sure, but there nonetheless with his barrel of whiskey, just twelve months late.

Opposite: He heard the sound of pipes, which played a fine tune, and there in front of him were dancers, women in silk dresses, bowing and twirling.

And they sat up that night, the man and his friend, and each of their wives, and what a Christmas Eve they had with that barrel of whiskey, which had mellowed with the warmth of the fairy hill, and they drank it all, just twelve months late.

A Dead Wife Among the Fairies

THERE ONCE WAS A MAN who lived with a wife he loved. They had been married for many years, and they made their home in a lighthouse, on the rocky coast by the sea. The waves threw up a spray but never dampened them, for they were sealed tight in their little world inside that lighthouse, and they lived happily there together, needing little else but the other. And so they lived, working together and talking all the day, lighting their beacon in the mists and fogs which fell over the sea like a woollen blanket.

Then one day, the good wife died, and she was buried in the hillside, under the rocks. And on those rocks the man sat each day, never lighting his beacon when the mists and fogs fell over the sea, staring instead at the rock which marked her grave, which marked the end of his life too. And so it was that he became a little mad, and went to see a witch, a fairy midwife who practised the magic of the earth and who could tell him how to get her back, his wife that he loved so well.

He saw her in her cottage, over the hill and across the brae, and she shook her head, and warned him to leave the dead with the fairies, for after death there can be no real life on earth, where the light would turn into dust any mortal who tried to return. But for the poor widowed man there could be no real life either, and so he begged the fairy witch to tell him her secrets and at last she did.

He was to go, she said, to a cave at the brae of Versabreck, on the night of a full moon, and he should take with him a black cat, and a Bible, and a thick wooden staff. There he must cry for his wife, and read to her from the psalms, and when he heard her voice once more, he must throw in the black cat and wait quietly for her to appear. Now the fairy folk would never let a mortal who had died pass back to his own land, so they would rally round her, and fight to keep her in their dust-webbed cave, which led to the Land of Light. The staff was to beat them with, for they could be sent back into their cave by the force of his will.

The moon waned and then it waxed again, and soon the night of the full moon arrived. The man was shivering with the fear of seeing his wife once more, yet he longed to touch her body, to feel her warmth, to hear her tender voice, so he steeled his quivering nerves and set off for the cave at the brae of Versabreck, and under his arm he held a black cat, and a Bible and a thick wooden staff. There he cried for his wife, and he read to her from the psalms, and when he heard her voice once

Opposite: They made their home in a lighthouse, on the rocky coast by the sea, where the waves threw up spray but never dampened them.

more, he threw in the black cat and waited quietly for her to appear.

Now the fairy folk fought for their mortal princess, and struggled to keep her in their dust-webbed cave, which led to the Land of Light, but he beat them with his staff, and sent them back into their cave by the force of his will.

And there was his wife, paler to be sure, and nothing more than skin and bones, but she smiled her same familiar smile, and although her body held no warmth and she smelled rather sour, he held her to him once again and heard her tender voice. And together they walked to their lighthouse home, snug in a warm embrace, and they lit their beacon in the mists and fogs which fell over the sea like a woollen blanket. When day broke, his wife was safe in the fairy cave again, for light would turn to dust any mortal who tried to return from the dead. And so her husband would watch carefully as the moon waned and then waxed, when they could meet again.

Opposite: His wife was paler, to be sure, and although her body held no warmth, and she smelled rather sour, he held her to him and together they walked to their lighthouse.

＊ ＊ ＊

LEGENDS OF GHOSTS

From ghoulies and ghosties and long-leggety beasties
And things that go bump in the night,
God Lord, deliver us!
ANONYMOUS

n Scotland, stories of ghosts and evil-spirits form a
rich and vibrant tradition, as alive today as it was
centuries ago. It is one of the oldest genres of Scottish
mythology and certainly the most enduring, for as
little is known today as it ever was about where we go
when we leave this earth. Our spirits may visit the realms of
heaven, but we have religion to explain that. What of that
time before the soul leaves the body? And what of the body
in the ground? The dank, dark earth houses many secrets,
and it is there that ghosts and other spirits are bred. The
newly dead and the long-dead are the most frightening, for
they are most venomous in their attacks on unsuspecting
family, or even strangers. Beware of a fleeting glimpse of
something unknown; watch out for that unexplained flash
of light in a haunted house; take note when a chair moves
suddenly in an empty room. And if a body is laid out for
burial in a house near to you, sleep elsewhere, for the spirits
of the dead can come back, in many strange forms. There's
no doubt of that, as these stories will tell.

The Fiddler of Gord

THERE ONCE WAS A MAN who lived in Sandness, near Papa Stour. He was a fisherman by trade, but he was known across the lands for the tunes he played on his fine fiddle. Folk came for miles to hear his music, and he could dance and sing a bit, so making it a real evening for anyone who cared to join in.

Now one cold night he left his cottage home, which was nestled in the base of a knoll, sheltered from the winds which burst over the hills from the sea. He left that night grudgingly, for the fire was warm and the company merry, but the larders were empty and more fish must be got by morning. So out he went into the frosted air, which crisped his breath and crunched under his feet. And on to his cold, dark boat he climbed, then out to sea, where he settled himself under oilskins and drew out his fine fiddle and began to play. And the Fiddler of Gord, as the man was called, played for hours as the fish drew closer to hear the wondrous music, catching themselves in his nets, but fighting not at all, so comforted were they by the strains from his fiddle.

Then the fiddler headed homewards, his basket groaning with fresh fish, tastier for having expired happily. As he passed the grassy knoll that hid his sweet, snug cottage from the fierce winds, he heard a graceful melody, and stopping in his tracks and laying down his basket, he listened. There was a light which glinted and beckoned through the grass and he was drawn towards it, as the music grew louder.

A door had opened in the hill, and from inside came the enchanted music of the fairy folk, a melody so divine and simple that his heart grew larger in his breast and he pulsed with pure pleasure. The Fiddler of Gord entered the door that night, and it was shut firmly behind him.

The cottage, tucked into the base of the knoll, was quiet as the night grew longer and the fiddler had not returned, and finally, when it neared dawn, the youngest son was sent out with a lantern, and when he returned with the fiddler's basket of fish there was no doubt in their minds

Opposite: *They searched for the Fiddler of Gord, scouring the rocky coasts for a sight of him. But when they found his basket of fish, there was no doubt that he had gone forever.*

that he'd been blown down the cliffs into the sea. The family lived there for many years, but the fiddler did not return. Finally, they moved from that place to another, and a new family took over the wee cosy cottage tucked into the base of the knoll, and they made a happy home there, warmed by the hearth and protected from the angry winds by the arm of the hillock.

It was on one windy night, when the sky howled at the thundering clouds, that a knock was heard on the door of this warm cottage, and when the door was opened there appeared an old man, bent and cold, and he thrust his hands at the fire, laying his fiddle to one side. And as he looked around he realized that it was not his family who gazed at him with astonishment, but another, and they wore garments which spoke of ages to come, not those he had come to know.

The children who played at the feet of the chairs came to gawk, and he asked, with all the rage he could muster, 'Where is my family? This is my house' to which the new family all laughed and called him mad and a coot from the whiskey barrel.

But the old grandfather of the family stayed silent, and then, at length, he said quietly to their indignant guest, 'Where do you hail from, man?' And when the Fiddler of Gord explained, the grandfather nodded his head slowly and said, 'Yes, you did live here once, but a man of your name disappeared, gone a hundred years now.'

'Well, where are my folk then?' whispered the Fiddler of Gord, his face a mask of confusion and fear.

'Dead,' came the reply, and the room was quiet once more.

'And so I'll join them,' said the fiddler, and drawing himself up to his full height he left the glow of the hearth, and the warmth of the family, and he headed to the top of the hillock, where the winds blew cold and frosty, crisping his breath and crunching under his feet, and he was followed by the wee lad of the house, who hid behind a bush at the base of the hillock to watch.

And there, in a glorious symphony of sound the fiddler played a rich and moving song that tugged at the chords of the wee lad's heart and filled his eyes with burning tears. And those tears burnt the melody into his memory, and it remained there until he died. Then the fiddler looked over at the northern star and played the tune once again, and collapsed, his fiddle flying over the hilltop into the sea.

And when the bairn summoned the courage to creep over to the old man, he found there a body of one who had died near one hundred years earlier. So he crept away home again, all the while humming a song that would haunt him till his dying day, blinded by tears and seeing not the door of a magic kingdom which had opened to welcome him to its timeless light.

MacPhail of Uisinnis

MORE THAN THREE CENTURIES ago there lived a man in Uisinnis, and his name was MacPhail. He was a big man, strong and silent, and he lived in a great stone house with his wife, his son, his son's wife, and their daughter. Now woe had fallen upon the family some thirteen years earlier when the daughter of MacPhail's son had been born dumb. Never a word had crossed the tongue of the young lass, but she was quiet and kind and well-liked by all.

The sad day came when old MacPhail died, and his body was dressed and laid at the end of their great stone house in preparation for burial. And his son, dressed in the black of mourning, drove off that day, to tend to the arrangements and gather together the old man's friends. He would be gone for a day, leaving the three women alone.

Opposite: Folk came from miles around to hear the music of the Fiddler of Gord, and he could dance and sing a bit, so making it a real evening for anyone who cared to join in.

That night, as the moon hung high in the sky, lighting the path to the great stone house, and setting the rooms aglow with its beams, a scuffling was heard from the room with the body, and as the noise grew much louder, there came a shriek.

And from the mouth of the dumb girl who had never before spoken a word, came the cry, 'Granny, Granny. My grandfather is up, and he's coming to get you! He'll eat you, he will, but he won't touch me.'

And the old woman flew from her bed, and sure enough, there, striding down the hall was the man who had laid at the end of the hall, dead and about to be buried. And she slammed her door, and thrust the wardrobe against it, and the boxes and piles of mending. She screamed with fright, but the door was shut tight.

Then, at this, the old MacPhail bent down and began to dig. And he dug there for some time, his great hands heaving earth and rocks from under the doorframe, until a tunnel was bored straight under the door. And as he wedged his way into this space, and thrust his mighty shoulders up the other side, his face a mask of horrible pain and determination, a cock flew down from the rafters, on to the floor. And there he crowed three times, and returned to his loft.

And old MacPhail ceased his digging then, and he fell deep into the trough he had dug, stone dead.

His son returned to Uissinis the following morning, and there he found a wife and a mother who could hardly utter a word, and a daughter who could not stop speaking of the ghost that had come. And thinking them all quite mad, he was stopped short in his tracks by the sight of his father, his hands torn and bloodied, half of him in a hole under his mother's door, and half of him out.

Old MacPhail was buried the next day, but the hole he had dug beneath that doorway is still there, in the ruins of that ancient house, and there's been no one able to fill it. 'MacPhail's Pit' is its name, and the spirit of that man lies within it to this day.

Opposite: The family MacPhail were dressed in the black of mourning, and the old woman and the dumb child sat in the great, silent stone house, deep in sadness.

Tarbh Na Leòid

ON THE ISLAND OF HEISKER, just west of Uist, lies an enchanted loch. Here lived a water-horse who was so terrible that everyone feared he would enter the village and destroy them all. And so it was that an old

man in the village who knew of such things advised his neighbours to raise a bull, one to each household, and never let it out until it was needed.

For many years, the village was safe. Women washed their clothes at the loch in pairs, for everyone knew that the water-horse would only strike if you ventured to the loch alone. And every household had a bull, never let out in the event that it would be needed. But so it was one year, that the villagers had become a wee bit complacent about the water-horse, and women began to be a little less careful about doing their laundry in pairs. And one day, for whatever the reason, a woman washed alone there, and when she finished, she laid down on the banks of the river and slept there.

The sun was high in the sky, and she was warmed into a deep slumber. When she woke, she saw a magnificent man standing there, the sun glinting on his golden hair, and lighting his clear blue eyes. He spoke to her then, about the fineness of the afternoon, and she spoke back.

'You must be very tired, after all that washing,' he said kindly, and the woman blushed, for the men of Heisker never cared much about a woman's tiredness, or about the washing.

'I am indeed,' she stammered.

'Do you mind if I join you there?' He smiled at her. 'Because I am pretty tired myself.'

'Oh, no,' she said sweetly, and made room beside her.

Now that fine young man sat down beside her, and then spoke again.

'Do you mind if I lay my head in your lap?' he whispered, and the woman flushed again and shook her head.

And so it was that this young woman was sitting by the sunny banks of the loch with the head of a handsome young man in her lap. And as she gazed down, hardly believing her good fortune, she noticed sea-dirt in his hair, and weeds, and bits of water-moss. And only then did she notice his hooves, which lay crossed in slumber.

The water-horse.

And carefully, ever so gently, the woman took from her washing bag a pair of sharp scissors, and cutting a hole in her coat where the water-horse's head lay, she slipped out from under him, leaving a bit of her coat behind.

And then she ran back to the village, and as the fear struck her, she shrieked to the villagers, 'Help, it's the water-horse.'

There was a neighing behind her, and the sound of hooves

Opposite: On the island of Heisken lies an enchanted loch. Here lived a water-horse so terrible that for miles around no one would venture to the loch alone.

on gravel, and she ran all the faster, calling for help.

Now the old man heard her first, and he called out to his neighbour, a man named MacLeod, whose bull was the closest. The bull was called Tarbh na Leòid, and he was a fierce creature, all the more so for being kept inside all his life.

'Let loose Tarbh na Leòid,' cried the woman, rushing into the village. 'Turn him loose!'

And so the bull was let loose, and he threw himself at the water-horse and there ensued a fight so horrific that the villagers could hardly watch. And it carried on for hours, and then days, and finally the bull beat that water-horse back to the loch, and they both disappeared.

The woman returned to her home, and she laid down on her bed, never to rise again.

Nor did the bull or the water-horse, although it is said that the horn of Tarbh na Leòid rose to the surface of the water one fine day, many years later. It's still there, they say, guarding the path to the loch of the water-horse.

Opposite: Women washed their clothes at the loch in pairs, for everyone knew that the water-horse would only strike if you travelled there alone.

❋   ❋   ❋

ORIGIN AND DIDACTIC LEGENDS

I had rather believe all the fables in the legend,
and the Talmud, and the Alcoran,
than that this universal frame is without a mind.

FRANCIS BACON

The legends which tell of the genesis of the earth, of the countryside, and its inhabitants may seem wild and unlikely, but for many centuries they were used to account for landmarks, and the origins of creatures. For man has always longed to make sense of his beginnings, to give a formula to the chaos from which we began, and if a hill resembles the footprint of a giant, there's every reason to believe there was once one there. Didactic legends, too, seem far-fetched at times, but the moral is always clear – if you live by the rules, you are safe from the clutches of witches and fairy-folk; if you eat well, you'll have good luck. The simplicity of the message is engaging, but the strictures they put upon daily life were not, for men lived whole lives in fear because of a dirty deed done in childhood, or a curse flung casually by an unhappy neighbour. But so it was that all good boys ate their porridge, and hung a bit of rowan over a door, and treated their wives with kindness. For no one knew who might visit them next, and what that visit might mean.

Dubh a' Ghiubhais

IT WAS MANY HUNDREDS of years ago, long before the days when stories were written down, that Scotland was covered in a great dark forest. This was a forest of fir trees, tall and fine as any to be seen, and there lived there a colony of people who made the trees their friends. Trees can be good friends indeed, for they spread their arms across the land, protecting it from the wind that blows from the stormy coasts, and the rain which is carried on its back. And they make homes for the wee folk, and animals of the forest, and wood for the houses and fires of the men who live there.

Now this fine forest was much admired, and there was one in particular who was very envious of Scotland's great dark trees. He was the king of Lochlann and he wanted more than anything to destroy them. He would pace round his castle, overcast and gloomy as the winter sky, and he would lament his unhappy lot, ridden right through with jealousy as hot as any good peat fire.

It was his daughter, the princess, who had watched this curious pacing for years on end who finally came to find out the cause of his unhappiness. He explained that he wished to find a way to destroy the trees of the Scottish forest; and that wee princess, she was a practical lass, and she said there was nothing for it but to do it herself.

And so it was that she bade her father leave to find a witch to put her in the shape of a bird, and when he'd done that, and when she'd become a beautiful, pure white bird, she set out over the grassy hills of Lochlann to the deep fir forests that carpeted the Scottish land. On the west coast of Scotland she came down, and there she struck a tree with a wand she had under her wing. With that single motion the tree would burst into flames and burn there, and it was not long before this beautiful white bird had burnt a great number of trees in that forest.

Now this beautiful white bird was no longer fair or pure; indeed, the smoke of the pinewood had cast an ugly black shadow across her feathers and she came to be known by the people of the country as the Dubh a' Ghiubhais, or Fir Black. And so it was that this Dubh a' Ghiubhais flew across the land, causing damage that robbed the wee folk of their homes and sent the animals scattering for shelter, and the men had no wood for their homes or their fires, and the trees could no longer spread their comforting arms across the land, protecting it from the wind that blows from the stormy coasts, bringing the rain on its back.

Opposite: The king of Lochlann paced around his castle and he wanted more than anything to destroy the great dark forest that carpeted the hills and valleys of Scotland.

And it was for this reason that the men of the land grouped together and decided that this bird must be stopped, for the Dubh a' Ghiubhais had brought sadness and rain to their sheltered lives.

It was not easy to catch the Dubh a' Ghiubhais, but it was heard, somewhere on the west coast of Scotland, that the bird had a soft, sweet heart in that blackened breast, and that a plan could be made to capture it.

And so it was that a man at Loch Broom hatched the plan, and on the very next morning spent a day at work in his barnyard, taking mother from her young all across the barn. For the piglets were taken wailing from their sows, the puppies barked as they were snatched from their mothers' teats, the foals were taken from mares, the lambs from sheep, the calves from the cows, the chickens from the hens, the kittens from the cats, and even the kids from the goats that grazed on the tender shoots of grass on the verge. And the uproar that followed was enough to churn the stomach of any man alive, for there were cries so piteous, so plaintive, so needing that the men and women for miles around hid themselves under soft down pillows in order to block out that dreadful sound.

It was not long before it reached the ears of the Dubh a' Ghiubhais, who was passing on her fiery course of devastation. And her soft, sweet heart nearly burst with pity for these poor creatures. She flew at once to the ground, and drawing her wand from beneath her wing she made as if to set the animals free when a small sharp arrow stung her breast, piercing her heart and bringing a clean, cold death. And the man at Loch Broom picked up his quiver and slinging it over his shoulder, bent over to collect the dead bird.

And so it was that the Dubh a' Ghiubhais was hung from a tree, where folk gathered round to cheer her death. News of what had happened reached her father, the king of Lochlann, and he was torn with grief and guilt. He sent his hardiest crew in a great long boat to bring the body of his dear daughter home. But there were fearful gales which pitched and jolted the ships that carried the funeral pyre, and although the brave sailors tried three times, they could get no further than the mouth of the Little Loch Broom.

Opposite:
And it was for this reason that the men of the land grouped together in a village home, and decided that the bird must be stopped.

And so it was that the Dubh a' Ghiubhais was buried beneath the tree where she hung, at Kildonan, at the bend of the loch at Little Loch Broom. She rests there still, a single fir tree growing atop her grave, which lies beneath a grassy green hillock.

The Pabbay Mother's Ghost

THERE ONCE WAS A MAN who lived in a cottage in Pabbay, a kindly man who knew a woman's needs and saw to them in the course of every day. And so it was that when this kindly man's wife was in childbed, he made for her a great steaming bowl of porridge with butter. For the oats and butter in the porridge would make her strong, and the baby would be born without a murmur.

This man sat by the fireside that night, stirring the porridge and reaching across occasionally to mop the brow of his sweet, dear wife. And then a woman came in and sat by him on his bench, and she asked quietly for a bowl of the steaming porridge with butter. The man handed her the bowl without a word and carried on stirring, reaching across occasionally to mop the brow of his sweet, dear wife. And when the woman returned her bowl empty he filled it once more, and then again, until the woman had three great pots of porridge with butter. But still the man made no sound, passing another bowl across to his wife now and then, reaching across occasionally to mop her sweet, dear brow.

And then the woman stood up, and she said to the man, as he stirred his porridge, 'There, that's what I should have had when I was in childbed myself, for I am strong now, and my baby would have been born without a murmur. It was hunger that was the cause of my death, but now, as long as a drop of your blood remains, no woman shall ever die in childbed if anyone who tends her with porridge and butter is related to you.'

So the woman left the cottage in Pabbay, and it was not long before the man's baby was born without a murmur, and his sweet, dear wife sat up strong and healthy in the childbed. And from that time on, not a wife or child of his, or a wife or child of his children died, for like their forefather, they knew a woman's needs and saw to them in the course of every day.

Luran

THERE ONCE WAS A CROFTER and his wife, and they lived in a glen far from the prying eyes of neighbours. They were quiet folk, but they lived well, with a herd of cattle to be envied, and a good bit of land. Their house was snug and warm in the coldest months, they had cream and milk and butter, and they wanted for nothing, in that glen, far from the prying eyes of neighbours.

Opposite: Their house was tucked in a glen, far from the prying eyes of neighbours and snug and warm in the coldest months.

Now that crofter was a healthy man, and he liked nothing more than a good meal, particularly if it was a feast of his favourite oakcakes, smeared with butter and dipped again in cream. And he partook of this kind of meal on most days so he grew rather heavy and clumsy. But their house was safe from any kind of danger, being far from the prying eyes of neighbours, and he grew perhaps a little too satisfied, and a little too complacent in his happy home.

For it was a cold Hallowe'en evening that strange things began to happen on the land of that satisfied crofter, and although everyone living near the fairy folk knows that Hallowe'en evening is their time for mischief, the crofter had not had cause to worry before this particular Hallowe'en night.

It was just as he was settling himself and his wife into their beds that they heard the howling of their guard dog, and a rumpus going on in the henhouse. And then they heard the cattle lowing, and everyone knows that cattle never low in the dead of night, so the crofter and his wife grew alarmed. Then he put back on his outdoor clothes, and he lit a lantern and headed towards the barnyard.

There, an astonishing sight met his eyes, for the barnyard was empty, his cattle gone, his pig sty clean, his henhouse bare. And the crofter sat down and held his head in his hands, and he asked himself how such a thing could happen to a house tucked so neatly in the glen, far from the prying eyes of neighbours. And then he started, for there was the sound of a lowing cow just over the knoll, and when he looked more closely there were tracks heading there too.

And so it was that the crofter plucked up his courage that Hallowe'en night, and went over that knoll, into the realm of the fairies. He crept there silently, until he heard voices. Then he stopped and he listened.

'Luran didn't run,' came a voice.

'Didn't run at all,' said another.

'Couldn't run at all,' giggled the first, and then there was a great deal of scuffling and laughter.

'If only his bread were not so hard,' said the other, 'but if Luran were fed on porridge, Luran would outrun the deer.'

And the crofter heard this conversation, and filled with fear (for everyone knows that fairies who speak English are the most dangerous of all) he peeked over the hilltop. There sat two smug fairies and just beyond them were his cattle, and all the livestock of the barnyard. He

Opposite:
There an astonishing sight met his eyes, for the barnyard was empty, his cattle gone, his pig sty clean and his henhouse bare.

sat back again, Luran the satisfied crofter, and he began to think.

And when he returned home to greet his anxious wife, he was still thinking, and again in the morning when she offered him his favourite meal of oatcakes, smeared in butter and dipped again in cream. And so it was that Luran held up his hand and said to his wife, 'You'll have to give me porridge and milk every day.'

As the days shortened and then lengthened again, Luran grew long and lean, and a fine, fit sight of a man he was. He worked on his farm and he raised more cattle, and on that house in the glen, far from the prying eyes of neighbours, Luran plotted his revenge.

It was twelve months now, and Luran was ready. Hallowe'en night found the crofter hidden in the stable of cattle, peering restlessly across their troughs. He was soon rewarded, for in popped the same two fairies who had visited there before, and as they led the first cattle away from his barn, Luran leapt up and chased those fairies over the knoll. And when he caught them, not far from the top, they gazed at him in surprise, and danced a fairy dance of approval.

So the crofter returned to his cosy house, leading his cattle back to the stable. And never again did those fairies trouble that house, tucked in the glen, far from the prying eyes of neighbours, for the master of that house ate nothing but porridge and milk, as all good men should.

The Hugboy

THERE ONCE WAS A GIANT, a hugboy he was called, and he lived with his wife somewhere near Caithness. Now they fought a great deal, that hugboy and his wife, and when they stamped their feet and howled, the little folk scurried for cover, for it was likely that a boulder or two could be thrown in their direction, or a mighty foot placed firmly upon a house or farm. Some say it was at that time that the fairy folk went to live inside the hills, for only then were they safe from the rages of the hugboy and his wife.

Well, so it happened, one dark day, that the hugboy fell out with his wife, and having had enough of his tempers, and with one of her own to match, she set out from home, never to return.

The hugboy was furious, for he chased her north, stepping through the Pentland Firth, and when he caught sight of her once more he threw a great stone at her. She was nearly flying now, so furious

and fast she was making away from the hugboy, and up Ireland Brae she ran as he threw another great boulder that missed its mark. But that stone still lies in the field above Ramsquoy, and his great fierce fingermarks are in it still. She ran still further, the wife of the hugboy, for there is another stone he threw at her in the Lylie Banks at Skaill in Sandwick.

But that's where he lost her, and the hugboy stopped his chase and set about finding some turf to build himself a new home, so far had he come from his old one. He stomped further north, scooping up handfuls of turf and placing them in his great straw basket. One handful carved out the Loch of Harry, and another made the Loch of Stenness. And then going back to lay the foundations of his great new house, he tripped, and stubbed his toe, whereupon a great bit of turf fell off that is now Graemsay. His toe fell off, too, and it forms a hillock that is mossed but cannot hide the fact that it was once a part of the hapless hugboy.

It was here that his great basket gave way, tipping its contents over the land. Now that giant had never had such a bad day, and in disgust he left the contents of his basket strewn as they lay, and that is what became the hills of Hoy. He turned towards home now, rubbing his sore head, stopping occasionally to adjust a sandal over his sore foot, and lamented his unhappy lot. For who could be so unlucky as to have lost a wife and a toe in one day.

The Three Questions of King James

THERE ONCE WAS A SCOTTISH PRIEST, a man adored by his flock, but not by the King himself; King James he was, and not an easy man to please. Well, this priest had crossed the path of the King and in the course of doing so had managed to offend him. And so it was decreed that the priest would be hung by his neck at the palace at Scone.

The poor kind priest had accepted his lot, when word came that there had been a partial reprieve. For if that priest would come along to Scone, and sit there with the King, and answer three questions that the King would put to him, he would be free to go home, to preach among his flock once more.

Opposite: The Scottish priest was to be taken to the palace of King James and there he would be hung by his neck for his sins.

Now questions are difficult things, for there are some that have no answers at all, and some that can be put in a way that even the wisest man on earth could find no answer. And although the priest was

SCOTTISH MYTHS & LEGENDS

a clever man, and he knew from the top to the bottom his great black Bible, he knew there would be traps, for who would let a man free on the back of three easy questions.

So he mulled over this dilemma, and he hummed and he hawed, and it was many days that he paced round his country cottage, and tapped his head, and sighed.

And then his brother, who lived with him and who was known to all as the simpleton he was, said, 'What is making you so catty?'

'Och, what use is it telling you, you're a simpleton no doubt.'

'Ahh, but can I not hear your problem? Maybe I can help?'

Now the priest thought little of this offer of help, but he was at the end of his frayed wits and he poured out his story to the simpleton man. He explained he was to be executed, and that there would be three questions put to him which could save his life.

'Hmmm,' said his brother, 'there are, you know, questions that just can't be answered.'

'I know it, I know it,' said the priest, shrugging unhappily. 'What am I to do?'

Now the priest was a good man, and even his simpleton brother could see this. 'I am going in your place,' he said firmly.

'Oh no. How can a fool like you answer questions that may not have answers?' asked the priest.

'Well it seems to me that if you are killed I will die too, for how can a simpleton live on his own. If I am executed in your place, what is the difference?'

So the priest agreed finally that his brother should go in his place, and so he draped his habit over the simpleton and handed him his staff. A prayer was said on his head and then the simpleton set off for Scone.

When he arrived, he was greeted by a man in a fine uniform, gold and blue and red, and he gravely ushered the priest's brother into the grand hall, for they had been expecting him, and the King was waiting. So the priest's brother was taken then to the King's room, where he sat on a throne that was more opulent than anything the young man had seen before. The room was hung with gold and jewels that winked and sparkled as the candles flickered in the breeze of his entrance. And the young man was enchanted by this fine sight, and he turned eyes at the stiff-faced King which shone as rich and true as any gem.

Now the king had chosen questions which were designed to trap the priest, for he cared not if he lived or died, and he settled back to watch the holy man's discomfort.

'You know why you are here,' he said gravely.

'Oh, yes,' said the simpleton in the priest's disguise.

'Well, then, let us begin. First question: where is the centre of the world?'

'Why, it's right here!' And the simpleton stamped the floor with his great staff.

'Oh!' The King looked surprised. 'I must let you have that one. Yes, I believe that you are right. For the world is a ball, and anywhere can be its centre. Yes, yes ...' he stroked his great beard, 'I'll let you have that one.' And then he continued, 'Next question: What am I worth sitting here, in all this,' he gestured round the room. 'Just what am I worth in money?'

'Well,' said the simpleton without hesitation, 'you are not worth anything more than thirty pieces of silver.'

'Why do you say that?' said the King with some consternation.

'Because the greatest man ever to enter the world was sold for only thirty shillings,' said the simpleton simply.

'Quite right,' blustered the king. 'I'll give you that one, too. Then the third question – and if you can answer this you'll be a free man ... Do you know what I am thinking now?'

And with that the King sat back, for there was no way that even a man of the cloth could know the kingly thoughts of a monarch.

But the simpleton blazed on. 'Why yes, I do,' he said.

'What's that, then?' said the King, sitting up with amazement.

'You think you are talking to a priest, and you are talking to a fool, his brother,' he said then.

And so it was that the stony King James rose from his throne to shake the hand of a simpleton, and then he laughed out loud.

'Be free man,' he said. Anyone who has a brother like that, and that brother a simpleton, deserves to be free. Away you go.'

✳   ✳   ✳

LEGENDS FOR CHILDREN

Between the dark and the daylight,
When the night is beginning to lower,
Comes a pause in the day's occupations,
That is known as the Children's Hour.

FROM *THE CHILDREN'S HOUR*, LONGFELLOW

he myths and legends told to children over the centuries were largely fictional, and they were developed to instil in children the kind of morality and superstition they would need to live a life of good fortune and good will. The legends were often violent, and many of the events that occurred were so frightening that a child would be shocked into a rigid belief, and good behaviour. For what child would not go straight to bed each night when he heard of the old fairy wife who comes with her brownie child? But there is a certain perverse morality there, too, designed to appeal to children. Bad mothers are punished, sometimes with death, and children can reign supreme in the fantasy world of the imagination. For when animals can talk, and a tall tale has a moral, anything is possible, and that magic is as strong today.

The Little Bird

A FAMILY ONCE LIVED IN THE WOODS, a man and a woman with their three small children. Now two of these children were boys, but the third was a wee slight girl with a smile that lit the hearts of all who met her. Her face was fair and her eyes held the promise of many dreams, but her mother, who had no time for those dreams, threw up her hands in despair at her fairylike daughter.

Their cottage was set deep in the woods, and it was a walk indeed to fetch milk from the farm down the hillock. But that wee slight girl was sent on that walk, with her mother's good jug, every day from the time she could toddle, and so it was that she would make that walk again on this particular day.

Now the girl had just counted five years, and on the table, laid there surely by the wee folk, was a bright shiny skipping rope, with handles as red as the flowers that gazed into the stream. And the girl wanted nothing more than to skip with that new rope, and to hold those red handles, but it was time, as it always was in the middle of the morning, to fetch the milk from the farm down the hillock.

'Can I take my skipping-rope with me?' she asked, her eyes shining with excitement.

But her mother, who had no time for that excitement, threw up her hands in despair at her fairylike daughter. 'No, ye can't,' she said sourly, and turned back to her cooking.

'But I won't spill the milk, Mummy, I promise,' said the wee girl.

And because her mother was not the sort who liked a good chat, or indeed a wee girl with eyes that shone with the promise of dreams, she said tersely, 'Well, then. Ye can take the skipping-rope, but if ye spills so much as a drop of the milk, I'll kill ye.'

And so it was that the little girl took her new skipping-rope, and skipped pertly down the lane, over the hillock to the farm, the milk jug clasped tightly in a hand that also clutched the shiny red handles of the skipping-rope. She stopped at the farm, and her jug was filled, and her skipping-rope admired, and away she went home again, skipping with the jug in one hand.

But things being as they are with matters that involve milk jugs and skipping-ropes, it was not long before that jug was dropped and broken, and the wee girl sat sadly in its midst and sobbed.

Opposite:
Their cottage was set deep in the woods, and it was a walk indeed, through the woods and down the hillock, to fetch the milk.

Now the girl was a familiar figure down this forest road, and soon enough a woman came along who recognized her, and who knew of the girl's mother, who was a very stern woman indeed, having no time for the dreams that shone in the eyes of her wee lass. So this kindly woman took it upon herself to right the young thing, and she said to her then, 'Now come along with me. I've got a jug just the twin of yours there.'

Then the new jug was filled, and with her skipping rope folded carefully and tucked under an arm, the little girl went home without spilling even a drop of milk.

But her mother, whose eyes shone not with dreams but with spite, said, 'Where did ye get the jug?'

And the little girl said, 'It's our jug, Mummy, just the same as ye gave me.'

But she said, 'No, this one is different. My jug had a blue stripe and this one has a red one.'

And with that she killed the wee girl, wrapping that skipping-rope around her thin neck until she was blue and still, and then she baked her in a pie. And being near to dinnertime, it was not long before her father came in, and he asked for the wee girl, for he had a soft spot for her fairylike ways, and those eyes that shone with the promise of dreams reminded him of another wee child with those same bright eyes, and that child had been himself.

His wife shook her head. 'Och, she's out playing, let her be.'

'Should we not call her for her dinner?' asked her husband, surprised at this sudden leniency.

'Na, let her go then.'

So the man tucked into the pie, with morsels of meat so tender that he ate greedily. And then, as he cut into an even larger piece, he found a finger, with a small silver ring.

He looked at his wife in horror, and he said, 'This is my daughter's ring. Why is she in this pie?'

And his wife said then that she had killed her, for she'd broken their milk jug and spilled the milk.

'Now what have you done?' he cried, and made as if to kill his wife himself. But now that the lass was gone there wouldn't be a woman around the house to keep it spic and span, and to make great succulent pies, so he thought again, and said, 'Och, I'll let ye live.'

When the two sons came in they too were distressed by the death of their wee sister, and none could eat his dinner that day.

Time went by, and nothing changed in the cottage set deep in the woods, except they had a visitor, in the shape of a small brown bird, who peeped into the windows of the house for hours of each day, and who had eyes that shone with the promise of dreams. But with the windows misted with the heat of the fire, the boys and their father couldn't see those eyes, and so they would shoo away the wee bird.

But everyday, there it would be again, peeping into the windows of the house.

By the time Christmas came round, the boys had grown to love the wee bird who sat on the sill, and they fed it with crumbs and bits of seed. They were doing just that, on Christmas Eve, when a voice startled them from their play. It boomed down the chimney and when the two boys reached the hearth it grew quieter, almost plaintive.

'Brother, look up and see what I've got,' and so the first brother looked up and was met by a shower of toys and sweets.

And then came the voice once again, 'Brother, look up and see what I've got,' and when the next brother looked up, he too was met by a shower of toys and sweets.

Then, 'Father, Father, look up and see what I've got,' and down the chimney came a fine new suit, and a bag of tobacco, and as he was admiring that suit, a letter dropped down the chimney, and on

it was written the words, 'Open this letter two hours after Christmas night.'

And into the silence came the voice once more, 'Mother, look up and see what I've got,' and when the mother looked up she dropped upon her head a great stone and killed her dead.

When the two hours had passed, the father opened the letter, which said, 'Dear Father, this is your daughter. The spell is broken. Once I have killed my mother, I shall return on New Year's Eve.'

The days to New Year's Eve passed slowly, and the father and his boys were filled with fear of what might greet them, for the wee girl had been long dead, and cut into a pie at that. But on that New Year's Eve there was no sign of her, and they grew more and more worried and frightened. And then, there was a tap tap tap at the window, a pecking sound that was familiar to them all.

'Och, it's only the wee bird,' said a brother to the other, but they opened the window anyhow, and prepared to feed it some crumbs. It was then that the bird hopped into the kitchen, and turning to them with eyes that shone with the promise of dreams, said, 'It's me, I'm home.'

They all stood aghast, the father and his two boys, and then the father spoke tentatively, reaching out to stroke the smooth feathers of the little bird, 'But you're a bird now.'

'Yes,' said the little bird, 'but if you take my mother's pinkie ring and give it to me now, I'll come back as a girl.'

This they did, though it meant digging up the body of the wicked mother from her newly turned grave. But they returned with the ring, and presented it to the bird, who turned at once into a little girl.

And the girl drew herself up tall, and took the ring that had belonged to her mother, and the ring that had once been hers, and laid them safely away in a box, a reminder of what can happen to girls with skipping ropes, and mothers with no time for fairylike ways or dreams.

The Fox, The Wolf and The Butter

LONG, LONG AGO, when a fox could befriend a wolf without fear of becoming his midday meal, and when all animals and folk in the woods spoke Gaelic, there was a wee den set deep in the forest, and it was the home of a fox and a wolf who lived there together. Now this fox and this wolf were friends, and firm friends they were, but there would always be that shadow of mistrust that hung between them, for a fox is a wily creature, and it was then, too, even in the days when a fox could befriend a wolf without fear of becoming his midday meal.

The fox and the wolf walked together each day, along the path overhung by fronded green firs, and over the hills, to the beach. And there they would comb the shores for debris that had blown in from the sea. Often it was, too, that they'd find a choice bit of fish for their dinner, or a bit of salt pork that had fallen over the side of a poor seaman's ship.

And so it was one day that they walked together, along the path overhung by fronded green firs, and over the hills to the beach. And there they came across a great cask of pure white butter, cold and creamy and freshly churned. And what delight lit their beady eyes, and their tongues fairly dripped with anticipation of this creamy treat, all cold and freshly churned. They danced about it then, and said to the other, 'We'll hide it now, till we get a chance to take it home.'

And so the fox and the wolf struggled with this great cask, up the hill and partway along that path overhung by fronded green firs, where they dug a great hole and buried it. And then they went home.

When they woke the next morning, the wolf yawned, and

Opposite:
Every day they had a visitor, in the shape of a small brown bird, who peeped into the windows of the house for hours on end.

licked his lips, and thought of all that lovely pure white butter, and he said to the fox, 'Shall we bring it a little further today?'

But the fox shook his head. 'Oh no,' he said, 'not today. I am going away today.'

The wolf looked surprised. 'Where are you going?' he asked.

'I am going,' said the fox, 'to a Christening. And then I'll be back.'

So the fox went off and he was gone for near a whole day. And when he came back he was smiling and content, and he laid himself down on a cosy bit of the den as if to sleep.

'So you're back,' said the wolf to the fox.

'Yes,' he said.

'What name was the babe given?' asked the wolf.

'We called him Mu Bheul (About the Mouth),' said the fox, to which the wolf nodded sagely.

The fox and wolf settled down for the night, and the next morning the fox rose and made as if to leave. Now it was one thing for the fox to set out alone of a morning, but quite another for him to do it twice, and the wolf felt a funny kind of suspicion, as the shadow of mistrust that hung between them grew ever so slightly larger.

And he said to the fox, 'Shall we bring it a little further today, the cask of butter?'

But the fox shook his head. 'Oh no,' he said, 'not today. I am going away today.'

The wolf looked wary. 'Where are you going?' he asked.

'I am going,' said the fox, 'to a Christening. And then I'll be back.'

So the fox went off and he was gone for near a whole day. And when he came back he was smiling and content, and he laid himself down on a cosy bit of the den as if to sleep.

'So you're back,' said the wolf to the fox.

'Yes,' he said.

'What name was the babe given today?' asked the wolf.

'We called him Mu Leth (About Half),' said he.

'I see,' said the wolf, although he didn't, and as he settled down for the night he felt that shadow of mistrust growing larger still.

But the wolf wakened fresh and ready for the day, the thought of all that pure, creamy butter making him salivate. And he stood and stretched, and looked for his friend, the fox. But he was not there. So he looked around, outside the den, and the fox was just

Opposite:
The fox and the wolf walked together each day, along the path overhung by fronded green firs, across the hills to the beach.

setting off down the path overhung by fronded green firs, and he called out then, 'Fox, where are you going? Shall we bring it a little further today, the cask of butter?'

But the fox shook his head. 'Oh no,' he said, 'not today. I am going away again today.'

The wolf just looked. 'Where are you going today?' he asked.

'I am going,' said the fox, 'to a Christening. And then I'll be back.'

So the fox went off and he was gone for near a whole day. And when he came back he was smiling and content, licking his chops and smacking his lips. And he laid himself down on a cosy bit of the den as if to sleep.

'So you're back,' said the wolf to the fox.

'Yes,' he said.

'What name was the babe given today?' asked the wolf.

'We called him Sgrìobadgh a' Mhàis (Scraping the Bottom),' said he.

'I see,' said the wolf, although he didn't again, and as he settled down for the night that shadow of mistrust was firmly between them.

But he woke again the next morning fresh and hungry, and the thought of that creamy butter made him nearly swoon with expectation. And he said to the fox, his tongue dripping so that he could hardly speak, 'Shall we get it today, the cask of butter we hid?'

And the fox said, 'Yes indeed.'

And so it was that the fox and the wolf set off down the path,

overhung by fronded green firs, almost to the hills whereupon lay the shore. And they reached the spot where the great cask of butter was hidden, cold, creamy and freshly churned. They uncovered it then, and lifting off the lid, eager for a succulent pawful, they discovered it ... empty.

It was awful. They jigged and railed and danced a furious reel round that empty cask. And the fox was so puzzled, and so too was the wolf, for neither knew who had taken their butter.

'Well,' said the fox at last, when they lay down spent from their angry dance, 'this is very queer. For not another creature knew of this cask but you and I, dear wolf. And this terribly queer affair means only one thing to me, and that is this: that it was you or me who took that butter. And that is what I think:

If I ate the butter, and it was I
Chiorram chiotam, chiorram, chatam, chiorram chiù
But if you ate the butter and it was you,
A galling plague on your grey belly in the dust.

There was no great harm in the curse of the fox, for his words were empty, but the curse he had laid on the wolf was poison indeed, for his belly was empty and the butter was gone.

The Ainsel

DEEP IN THE HEART OF THE BORDER country, where the wind howls with cold, lived a wee boy called Parcie. He lived with his mother in a small, snug cottage where the fire burned bright and bathed the stone clad walls in a soft, cosy glow. They lived alone there for his father was long since gone, but they managed with little, living simply and happily among the trees and the wood folk who inhabited them.

Now like most small boys, Parcie plotted all day in order to avoid being sent to bed each night. He longed to sit by the hearth with his mother, watching the burning embers cast intriguing shadows which danced and performed a story that seemed to Parcie like it could go on forever. But each night it was cut short, as was the sound of his mother's mellifluous voice as she sang to him of fairies and sea-folk, and told of stories and legends of long ago. For it was it at this point that Parcie's mother would close up her bag of mending.

Opposite: They lived in a small cottage, deep in the heart of the border country, where the wind howls with cold.

'It's time for your bed, Parcie,' she would say, always the same thing, and Parcie would be packed neatly into his tiny box-bed where the fairies had laid a nest of golden slumberdust so potent that his eyes were shut and he was fast asleep as soon as his head touched his soft pillow. And there he'd sleep all the night, until the next morning he struggled to hatch a plan to stay awake all night, to carry on and on the drowsy contentment of the evening.

But one night Parcie's tired mother could argue no further and when the fire began to sink down into black-red embers, and she said, 'It's time for your bed, Parcie' he would not go. And so she picked up her mending, and tidied it away, setting a bowl of cool, fresh cream by the doorstep as she went along the corridor to her own bed.

'I hope to God the old fairy wife does not get to you, lad, but it will be your own fault if she does,' whispered his mother as she disappeared into her room.

And suddenly the warm red room took on a more sinister cast, and the shadows no longer told a story but taunted him, warning him, tempting him until he was a jumble of fear and confusion. And just as he steeled himself to dash to his warm box-bed, filled with golden slumberdust, a tiny brownie leapt from the chimney and landed on his foot.

Now brownies were common in the days when Parcie lived in the stone cottage with his mother, and they came each day to every house that had the courtesy and the foresight to leave a bowl of cool, fresh cream by the doorstep. And if some foolish occupant forgot that cream one night, she would be sure to find a tumultuous mess the next day. For brownies came to tidy everything away, neat and clean, collecting specks of dust and laying things just so, so that in the morning the lucky household gleamed with shining surfaces and possessions all in order.

But Parcie knew nothing of the magic that dropped through the chimney each night and he was surprised and rather pleased to see this tiny fairy. The brownie was not, however, so pleased to see Parcie, for he was an efficient wee brownie and he liked to have his work done quickly, in order to get to the lovely bowl of cool, fresh cream which awaited him by the doorstep.

'What's your name?' asked Parcie, grinning.

'Ainsel (own self),' replied the brownie, smiling back despite himself. 'And you?'

'My Ainsel,' said Parcie, joining in the joke.

And so Parcie and the brownie played a little together, and Parcie watched with interest while the brownie tidied and cleaned their cottage in a whirlwind of activity. And then, as he neared the grate to sweep away some dust that had come loose from the hearth, Parcie took an inopportune moment to poke the fire, and what should fly out upon the poor brownie but a red-hot ember which burnt him so badly that he howled with pain.

And then, into the snuffling silence that followed, a deep frightening voice boomed down the chimney. It was the old fairy wife who Parcie's mother had warned of, and she flew into a rage when she heard her dear brownie's tears.

'Tell me who hurt ye,' she shouted down the chimney, 'I'll get him, so I will.'

And the brownie called out tearfully, 'It was My Ainsel'. Parcie lost no time in hurling himself from the room and into his box-bed where the golden slumberdust did not cast its magic over the terrified boy, for he laid awake and shaking for a long time after his head touched his soft pillow.

But the old fairy wife was not concerned about Parcie, for she called out, 'What's the fuss, if you did it yer ainsel' and muttering she thrust a long brown arm down the chimney and plucked the sniffling brownie from the fireside.

Now what do you think Parcie's mother thought the next morning when she found her cottage spic and span, but the bowl of cream still standing untouched, cool and fresh by the doorstep. How perplexed she was when the brownie stopped visiting her cottage, although she always left a bowl of cream to tempt him. But in the heart of the Border country, where the wind howls with cold, bad is almost always balanced by good, and so it was then when from that night onwards, Parcie's mother never again had to say to him, 'Parcie, it's time for your bed,' for at the first sudden movement of the shadows, when the fire began to sink down into black-red embers, he was sound asleep in his tiny box-bed, deep in the sleep of the golden slumberdust.

✳   ✳   ✳

TALES OF
THE GREAT FÉINN

Unhappy the land that has no heroes.
LEBEN DES GALILEI, BRECHT

he great Féinn, or Fians as they are also called, were a fighting people born to battle. Fionn Mac Chumail was their leader, and they numbered nine thousand warriors, their army called the Host of the Fians. The Féinn belonged both to Eirinn (Ireland) and to Alba (Scotland) and every rolling hill in Scotland bears the scars of one of their deeds.

The Host of the Fians was set up when the Lochlannaich, or the Norwegians, as we know them today, ravaged the coasts of Eirinn and Alba, and the King of Eirinn prayed for a way to dispose of them. It came to him in a dream that he must marry the hundred most powerful men and women in the land, and let their children's children become the greatest army ever seen. These were the Host of the Fians, and Fionn Mac Chumail led them into battle against the Lochlannaich and drove them away forever.

The feats of the great Féinn, of the wise warrior Fionn, and his sons, Osgar and Ossian[1], form the basis of some of the most dazzling Scottish legends, for Scotland is a country of many great heroes, and storytellers like nothing better than to remember their deeds.

---

[1] Fionn is known in Scotland as Finn MacCool, and Fingal, depending on the part of the country, and there are many variations of the spelling of his surname. Ossian, from the Irish Oisin of the Fenian Cycle, has a different number of brothers in different legends, as well as variations in the spelling of his name.

The Story of Ossian and the Crow

LONG, LONG AGO, in the days of the great Féinn, there lived three brothers who made their home on the grassy hills of the Highlands. They lived apart, in three stone shelters, but they met often, hunting for deer that roamed wild across their land. These three brothers had not yet married, and women were scarce, in the grassy hills of the Highlands, in the days of the great Féinn, so they were always on the look-out for a good bit of lass.

Now Ossian was the eldest of the three brothers, and he had the wisdom and the kindness of all three, for his brothers were daft and selfish lads, and they lived for themselves.

It was a cold, stormy night, the kind of storm that brews all day on the Highlands, until the winds are fevered, and the thunder roars into the darkness. The rain was pelting against the stones of his brothers' shelters, and they huddled against their hearths for warmth. When suddenly, out of the night flew a great Black Crow, with feathers wet against her scrawny body. She flew to the shelter of the youngest brother, and tapped on the door. The crow spoke Gaelic, for all animals did, in the days of the great Féinn, and she begged sweetly for lodging for the night, and a bite of food.

'Och, be gone, Black Crow, or I'll off your head with my finger,' snarled the youngest brother. And the Black Crow flew off.

She was colder when she tapped on the door of the middle brother, and her feathers hung sadly against her tiny body. Her voice was plaintive, but pure, and she asked once again for lodging for the night, and a bite of food.

'Och, be gone, Black Crow, or I'll off your head with my finger,' snarled the middle brother. And the Black Crow flew off.

And when she arrived at Ossian's house she was so cold that her eyes were wild with pain and she could hardly move. Her feathers were useless now, and she could only hobble towards the door. Light shone from the window, and the Black Crow took heart. There was a warmth, here, she felt, and with that canny instinct of animals, especially those from the days of the great Féinn, she knew that she would be safe. When she finally reached the door, tapped upon it, and asked Ossian if she could have lodgings for the night, he greeted her with a great wide grin, and opened his door.

'Come in,' he said, and offered the poor Black Crow a bowl of food that steamed with goodness. She ate hungrily, and then again,

Opposite:
'I am here,' said the beautiful woman, 'and I can live here as your wife.' She smiled gently, and reclined with astonishing grace.

and finally sat back. Ossian, sensing she was tired, carried her gently to his upstairs room, and laid her on the bed. He returned, then, to the fire, where a blanket was warming, and carrying it back to the cold Black Crow, he stopped with a jerk.

For there, on the bed in his own room was the most beautiful woman he had ever seen. And she lay there sleeping, her hair spilling across the sheets, her pale white skin lit by the dew of a good night's rest. And as he neared the bedside to take a closer look, she rose, and opened her eyes – eyes that spoke of days gone by, of wondrous sights and eager dreams. Ossian was entranced.

'How, how do you come to be such a beautiful woman when you were but a moment ago a Black Crow?' he stammered, hardly daring to believe his eyes. He rubbed at them, but she was still there, a glorious vision.

'I've been enchanted,' explained the woman kindly, 'and until now, no one would take me in. Until someone gave me a bed and some food, I would have to live my life as a crow. But now,' and she gestured all around her, 'I am here, and I can live as your wife for as long as you never cast up at me the shape in which I arrived. If you do that,' and now her voice grew quiet, 'I will become a crow once again.'

So Ossian and his wife lived there together, to the envy of his oafish brothers, and the crow woman made his shelter a home like none other. Wee curtains appeared, with a soft cover for the bed, and a bit of flower from the hillside was laid on the table for their meals. And his wife blossomed with the attentions he gave her, and she offered him her rare knowledge and her perfect, sweet love.

Ossian went out most days, and hunted the deer which roamed wild on his land, but he always returned to his dear wife, and there was never a cross word between them, for he had remembered her warning and sought never to cast up at her the shape in which she arrived.

Now it was one cold winter's day, like many others, that Ossian prepared to go out for the hunt.

'That bitch should have puppies today,' he said, stroking the dog who lay curled in the corner. 'Put a string around the neck of the first puppy,' he said, and then he left.

He was not gone long when the first puppy was born, and his wife carefully tied a length of string round his neck. She put him to one side, and helped the bitch as more and more puppies were born. She had just put the last to its breast when there was a knock at the door.

Opposite:
There on the bed in his room was the most exquisite woman he had ever seen; she lay there sleeping, her hair spilling across the sheets.

Now this knock surprised Ossian's wife, for she had never, in all her time there, been visited on the grassy hills of the Highlands. For long ago, in the days of the great Féinn, people lived far from one another and it could be many months before they spied another man. But she rose, and swallowing the fear which surged up into her throat, she opened the door.

There stood a man as black as the night, his face a tortured mask.

'I want the first puppy,' he said. And he held out a hand that was grimed with the dirt of the afflicted. She jumped back, and went to fetch the puppy.

Now Ossian's wife was a clever lass, and she knew that her husband had wanted that first-born for himself. So she pulled the string from the puppy's slim neck, and placed it round the neck of another, and it was this dog that she presented to the great dark man at the door. He took the puppy, and lifted its ear. And then tugging on it, and shaking it, he was rewarded by the yelp of the dog.

'No,' he said, handing her back, 'she was not the first puppy.'

Then one by one Ossian's wife brought out the puppies, and with each one he took it in his hand, and lifted its ear, and then tugging on it, and shaking it, he waited for the inevitable yelp. And when the last puppy was given to him, for she had not told him of the tiny first-born she had hidden under the blanket by the hearth, he cast it aside and grabbed at her throat.

'The first puppy, or I'll cut off your head,' he said, his face so close

that she could count every blackened pore. She pulled back, and returned with the puppy. And he took hold of it and lifted its ear. And then, tugging on it, and shaking it, and then shaking it again, he smiled, for it had made no sound at all. He tucked that puppy under his arm and left, the great dark man, and he never did return.

Ossian's wife was pale and fearful when he returned home that night, and striding into the cottage as he always did, and taking her by the hands, he cried, 'The puppies, they've been born.' Then kneeling over the litter, he chose the one with the string tied round its neck. And he raised it up, lifting its ear, and then tugging on it and shaking it. When the puppy let out a fine whimper, Ossian turned to his wife with cold eyes.

'You've put the string round the wrong neck,' he said then. To which the wife of Ossian hung her head, and told him the story of the great dark man, and how he had threatened to cut off her head, and Ossian looked at her with such disdain that she was numbed with pain. She hardly felt the next blow, but his words worked their magic:

'What can I expect from a Black Crow,' he said coarsely. And then she was gone.

He called to her, then, did Ossian, who was torn by grief and wretched shame, but she could not come back. She called to him from the sky, 'I can never go back now. I told you on that first day. I gave you my warning.' And with that she thrust her beak at him, and there, suddenly in his hand lay a golden ring.

'Place that ring upon your finger,' she said softly, 'so that you may live forever. For you have given me many fine years, dear Ossian.' And the Black Crow disappeared forever.

That was how Ossian lived to an age beyond all others, for such things could happen, long, long ago, in the days of the great Féinn, when crows could become women, and then just disappear into the night.

Fionn and the Journey to Lochlann

Opposite: They flew across the rocky terrain, over lochs and rivers, under vast cliffs which threatened to belch rocks on to the travellers, and along moss-lined valleys.

IT WAS MANY YEARS since the Lochlannaich had been driven from the land of the Féinn, and Fionn and his warriors spent most of their time stalking deer on the rolling hills of the Highlands, still glorying in the days of war, but keeping their minds sharp with the hunt.

And it was on such a pursuit that Fionn and his men

stumbled upon the form of a young man, a stranger who hailed them from the hill, and asked to be taken as one of their party.

'Who are you lad,' asked Fionn kindly, for he was a man of great knowledge and wisdom and the folk of other countries, (this man spoke in an unfamiliar tongue) interested him greatly.

'I have come from great distance, seeking your company,' he said gravely, 'I need a master.'

'And I need a lad to serve me,' said Fionn. 'But what will you want for your pay, if I take you on for a year and one day?'

'Not much,' said the boy, 'just your company at a feast in the palace of the King of Lochlann, one year and one day from tonight. But you must come alone,' he said then, 'without dog, or man, or calf or child, or indeed any weapon.'

The great Fionn roared with laughter, for he enjoyed a good challenge, and he nodded now furiously, and shook the boy's hand.

'I like your terms,' he said with a great smile, 'for there is a hint of adventure there, something quite intriguing. That's it, then, join me for a year and one day and I shall journey with you to Lochlann.'

And so it was that the stranger became an attendant to Fionn, serving him loyally for a year and one day, learning a great deal about the fine warrior. He would watch Fionn, revel at his agile mind that tore strips from the wisdom of others.

For although Fionn was not the strongest of all warriors, his power lay in his gift for clear-headed sagacity, for fairness and honour, and for generosity and kindness. He travelled far and wide with his hound Bran, the finest hunting-dog ever seen, a huge animal whose loyalty to his master was the envy of every warrior of the great Féinn.

And Fionn was a man of his word, and when that year and one day had passed, quickly as it is wont to do, he stood by his promise to travel with the stranger to Lochlann, to feast at the palace of the king.

Fionn called together his warriors, and he told them of his plan, and although they all protested, and a mighty uproar ensued, he stood firm. But if Fionn liked adventure, and the scent of pure excitement, he was also practical, and he knew, deep down, that it was not a feast he would be attending at the palace in Lochlann, but more likely the funeral of someone he knew very well.

But he faced his men now, and he spoke to all nine thousand of them, gathered there to hear him:

Opposite: There stood a stark and ugly castle – the spray from the sea spattered it in a rhythm which taunted the visitors.

'I will go and honour my word. But if I have not returned, in one year and one day, then you shall know that I have been killed, and my blood spilled across the land. And if this comes to pass, there must be no man amongst you without a quiver of arrows or a sword in your hands. For my death shall be avenged on the strand of Lochlann, and the Host of the Fians shall reign supreme.'

And a great roar of approval broke out across the army as Fionn joined the stranger to fulfil his pledge. The mighty dog Bran was to be left behind, and Fionn stroked his great ears and whispered a fond farewell, but just as he was about to take his leave, the court fool beckoned him to one side.

'Sire, listen, great leader of the Féinn,' he whispered, 'take heed. For the wisdom of a king is often trapped in the mind of a fool, and I have that advice for you now.'

And as the powerful Fionn bent over to listen, he carried on.

'Take this. It's not dog, or man, or calf or child, or even a weapon. Take it.' And with that he thrust something in the pocket of Fionn, and stumbled off.

Fionn plunged his hand deep into his pocket and withdrew the treasure. It was the Bran's chain of gold, a lead which calmed the mighty dog and kept him by his master's side. And if Fionn was puzzled, he showed it not, returning the chain to his pocket and nodding silently.

And so his great journey began, and he departed in the steps of the

lad who had been his servant. Their travels were swift, for the boy had wings for feet, and he flew across the rocky terrain, over lochs and rivers, under vast cliffs which threatened to belch rocks on the travellers, and along bracken- and moss-lined valleys. And then, after many days of travelling, they reached their destination: the palace of the King of Lochlann.

There it stood, stark and ugly, thrust up from the grey rocks that veered crazily across the coastline. The spray from the sea spattered it in a rhythm that taunted the visitors, inviting them into the dirty depths of the castle. There was no opulence here, but blackness and evil, and Fionn knew then that he had been right. He would feast not tonight. Unwittingly, he reached into his pocket and touched Bran's golden chain.

He was led into the great hall where the King of Lochlann and his evil chiefs plotted his death. A cry surged forth when he entered, and he was flung against a wall and forced to sit down. With an ironic smile, Fionn Mac Chumail complied.

'Hang him,' shouted a group of black-bearded men.

'No, burn him,' shouted another.

'I say drown him,' shouted a lone voice, to which a rowdy cheer went up.

But then rose a man with a face as dark as the stormy seas, and he fair snarled his words to the eager crowd, 'There is only one death that will shame the noble,' and at this he spat to one side, 'Fionn Mac Chumail. Let us send him to the Great Glen, where he will be torn apart by the terrible Grey Dog. There could not be a death worse for the leader of the great Féinn than to fall at the cur of a dog.'

And so it was decreed that Fionn Mac Chumail would be sent to the Great Glen, a gloomy wilderness of black thorn trees and lichen-covered rocks, and he would meet his death there at the jaws of the most frightful dog on earth, the Grey Dog of Great Glen. This dog had teeth that were taller than most men, and a snarl that curdled the blood of even the bravest warrior.

So Fionn was left there alone that night, with the darkness pricking at his courage, and the baying of the hound, which echoed in the distance, tugging at his mind. And the great Fionn waited there, for to run would be useless. In one direction lay the bloodthirsty Lochlannaich, in the other, the cruel Grey Dog.

So he stood his ground, as it was his nature to do, and he prepared to face his death as the hero he was.

Opposite: The two great dogs, Grey Dog and Bran, had long ago given up hope of meeting again, and they frolicked together now, on the grassy green knoll.

And then at once there was the dog, more terrifying than anything he could have imagined, for this great canine had a dripping tongue that hung over fangs like white spearheads, eyes that were filled with an instinctive hatred of all man, and hackles that stood up on his back like the finest wrought armour.

His breath was poison, and the stench and heat of it scorched the skin of Fionn and he staggered back.

And as he fell, his hand flew instinctively to his pocket, where he grasped Bran's golden chain. And as he drew it out, and waved it before him, the Grey Dog leapt on top of Fionn, who cursed his ill-fortune. But it was not the jaws of Grey Dog that found their mark, but his great thick tongue, which lapped at the breath-burnt warrior, and healed him there and then. And with his huge teeth he tugged gently at Fionn, righting him to his feet, and nudging him forward, and the light that shone from the eyes of that dog was no longer that of hatred, but loyalty, and love.

And it was a bemused Fionn who set out of the Great Glen with Grey Dog at his side. He knew not what had happened, but clasped Bran's golden chain round the great dog's neck, and carried on.

At the bottom of the Glen was a wee stone cottage, a humble sort of place that was home to an old man and his wife. Now the wife was at the stream, tending to her washing, when the strange couple rounded the bend,

and she flew back to the cottage, screaming and gnashing her teeth, certain that death was upon her, for had she not just seen a vision of hell itself?

And her husband rose unsteadily, and struggled to comfort her.

'But what have you seen?' he asked, failing to get any sense from her tortured words. But at last she could talk, and as she stumbled through sentences riddled with nonsense her fears became clear.

A great warrior, the most illustrious man she had ever seen, was making his way up their path, and who should be beside him but the Grey Dog himself.

At this the old man began to laugh, and he held himself up with pride.

'There is only one man in the world who could tame the Grey Dog, and that is Fionn Mac Chumail. We are honoured to have him on our land,' he said then.

And so the old man and his wife went out to greet Fionn, who told of his adventures at Lochlann. He was soon settled in their comfortable home, and fed with simple fare that warmed him to the root of his being. He became content there, that restless warrior, and delighted in the rare knowledge and insight of the old man. Night after night they sat by the roaring hearth, toasting their toes and sharing the stories of the past, and so Fionn learned how the Grey Dog had become tamed.

For the Grey Dog was lulled by the sight of Bran's chain because he was his brother, separated from him when the litter was young. And as Bran was loyal to Fionn, so too would be the Grey Dog, who in deference to his brother Bran, acknowledged Fionn as his master.

So it was that a year and one day soon passed in the pleasant company of this cottage in the Glen, and Fionn found a deep peace within himself, one which he would call upon often in the months to come.

But his peaceful stay did come to an end, as all good things do, and he was woken with a start one day, by the rallying cry of nine thousand men. He ran from the cottage, and across the knoll, and there, marching across the verge, was an army led by a strong, fierce man with flowing red locks.

Fionn's eyes pricked with tears. It was his own son Osgar, leading the Host of the Fians, and as he flew over the hill, with Grey Dog at his side, his army swarmed around him, cheering and shouting, hailing the great leader whose death they had come to avenge. And above the rejoicing could be heard the howling of two great dogs, for Grey Dog and Bran had long since given up hope of meeting again. They frolicked together now, licking and biting haunches, and rolling in the grassy green knoll.

'We have come,' say Osgar joyously, 'for it is a year and one day since you have left us, and we thought you dead.'

'I am alive, my dear son,' said Fionn solemnly, 'but only by my wits and the grace of a kind fool. For the Lochlannaich have plotted to kill me.' And with that he described his horrific ordeal.

Already fired for battle, the great Féinn needed little encouragement. They drew their swords and with tempers high, plunged across the land to the castle of the king of Lochlann, and there they began a massacre which turned the grimy foam of the deep grey sea red with blood.

And then they returned home again, the triumphant Féinn, but that is another story.

Fionn's Great Sword

AFTER THE DEATH OF DIAMAID at the hands of Fionn Mac Chumail, the great Féinn travelled far. Fionn himself struggled to put the past behind him, to forget his craven deed. They crossed over from Kintyre and hunted on Islay, and it was here that Fionn met with a strange man, who leapt into his path and stood firm.

'Fionn Mac Chumail,' said the wild little man, 'Come with me. For I am a blacksmith, and I'll forge you a sword like no other.' And with that he disappeared over the hillock, his voice echoing back, 'So catch me if you can.'

Now the great Fionn Mac Chumail liked nothing better than a challenge, and being as fleet of foot as any fairy, he joined in the chase. Over the hills they went, and across valleys, feet hardly touching ground. And as the fairy blacksmith leapt out of sight, the hardy Fionn followed close in his footsteps, catching him up once again. And so the chase went on for many hundreds of miles, the great Scottish warrior never losing his foot, never missing a beat.

And they arrived at last, landing on a hill outside a tiny stone cottage, and here it was that the fairy stopped, turning to congratulate Fionn. With a mischievous laugh, he invited him inside.

'Here is my smithy, great leader,' he said gleefully. 'You have matched me in speed and so together we shall go and forge you a sword worthy of your great stature.'

And they entered the cottage, where the blacksmith's fairy daughter blushed and curtseyed to the grand man who had entered their humble abode. And she plied them with food and drink, while Fionn lit the great fire and the blacksmith prepared his tools.

And so it was that a great bar of iron was held over the fire that roared and crackled, scorching the blacksmith, his daughter and Fionn himself. But they worked away, Fionn at the bellows while sweat poured from his noble brow, and the blacksmith with his tools, forging a sword fit for a hero.

When the sword was nearly finished, the blacksmith's daughter drew Fionn to one side.

'My father will fit the handle now, and he will ask you what else there is to do. Then, my lord, you must answer him, saying "The sword is wanting but one little thing yet" and then you must plunge your sword into his body. If it is tempered with fairy blood, your sword will be the mightiest ever made.'

So Fionn waited while the blacksmith worked, and soon enough he stopped and asked what else there was to do.

And Fionn grabbed the sword from the fairy blacksmith, whose face registered only mild surprise, and he plunged it into his body, through the ribs and out the other side. And as he drew it out again, the sword gleamed with the blood of enchantment. He left the house then, with the daughter tending to her slain father, and he joined his men.

And the great Féinn travelled on again, the powerful fairy sword safe by the side of the mighty Fionn. And his prophecy had been true, for wherever that sword was aimed, it struck its mark.

Opposite: Fionn Mac Chumail drew his mighty sword into the air, and from that time it never left his side.

The name of the sword was Mac an Luinne, and from that day onwards, it never left the side of the great Fionn.

✳   ✳   ✳

GLOSSARY

The following provides a guide to some of the words which may be unknown to some readers, along with some of the key personages and characters of Scottish myths and legends.

Bairn   Little child, also called bairnie.

Bannock   Oat or barley cake.

Bere   Barley.

Bodach   The terms means 'old man'. The Highlanders believed that the Bodach crept down chimneys in order to steal naughty children. In other territories, he was a spirit which warned of death.

Bran   In Scottish legend, Bran is the great hunting hound of Fionn Mac Chumail. In Irish mythology, he is a great hero.

Brigit   Scottish saint or spirit associated with the coming of spring.

Brollachan   A shapeless spirit of unknown origin. One of the most frightening in Scottish mythology, it spoke only two words, 'Myself' and 'Thyself', taking the shape of whatever it sat upon.

Brownie   A household spirit or creature which took the form of a small man (usually hideously ugly) who undertakes household chores, and mill or farm work, in exchange for a bowl of milk.

Cailleach Bheur   A witch with a blue face who represents winter. When she is reborn each autumn, snow falls. She is mother of the god of youth (Angus mac Og).

Caoineag   A banshee.

Cat   A black cat has great mythological significance, is often the bearer of bad luck, a symbol of black magic, and the familiar of a witch. Cats were also the totem for many tribes.

Cath Sith   A fairy cat who was believed to be a witch transformed.

Ceasg   A Scottish mermaid with the body of a maiden and the tail of a salmon.

Ceilidgh   Party.

Crodhmara   Fairy cattle.

Crow   Usually associated with battle and death, but many mythological figures take this form.

Cu Sith   A great fairy dog, usually green and over-sized.

Cutty   Girl.

Dog   The dog is a symbol of humanity, and usually has a role helping the hero of the myth or legend. Fionn's Bran and Grey Dog are two examples of wild beasts transformed to become invaluable servants.

Divots   Turfs.

Durk   Knife.

Each Uisge   The mythical water-horse which haunts lochs and appears in various forms.

Fairy   The word is derived from 'Fays' which means Fates. They are immortal, with the gift of prophecy and of music, and their role changes according to the origin of the myth. They were often considered to be little people, with enormous propensity for mischief, but they are central to many myths and legends, with important powers.

Fingal   Another name for Fionn Mac Chumail, used after MacPherson's Ossian in the eighteenth century.

Fionn Mac Chumail   Irish and Scottish warrior, with great powers of fairness and wisdom. He is known not for physical strength but for knowledge, sense of justice, generosity and canny instinct. He had two hounds, which were later discovered to be his nephews transformed. He became head of the Fianna, or Féinn, fighting the enemies of Ireland and Scotland. He was the father of Oisin (also called *Ossian*, or other derivatives), and father or grandfather of Osgar.

Fir Chlis   Nimble men or merry dancers, which are the souls of fallen angels.

Fuath   Evil spirits which lived in or near the water.

Gin   If.

Goodman   Man of the house.

Goodwife   Woman of the house.

Gruagach   A kind of brownie, usually dressed in red or green as opposed to the traditional brown. He has great power to enchant the hapless, or to help mortals who are worthy (usually heroes). He often appears to challenge a boy-hero, during his period of education.

Guidewife   Woman.

Henwife   Witch.

Houlet   Owl.

Kelpie   Another word for *each uisge*, the water-horse.

Ken   Know.

Knowe   Knoll or hillock.

Land of Light   One of the names for the realm of the fairies. If a piece of metal welded by human hands is put in the doorway to their land, the door cannot close. The door to this realm is only open at night, and usually at a full moon.

Lang syne   The days of old.

Leman   Lover.

Muilearteach   The Cailleach Bheur of the water, who appears as a witch or a sea-serpent. On land she grew larger and stronger by fire.

Onygate   Anyway.

Oisin   Also called Ossian (particularly by James Macpherson who wrote a set of Gaelic Romances about this character, supposedly garnered from oral tradition). Ossian was the son of Fionn and Sadbh, and had various brothers, according to different legends. He was a man of great wisdom, became immortal for many centuries, but in the end he became mad.

Pibroch   Bagpipe music.

Puddock   Frog.

Sabdh   Mother of Ossian, or Oisin.

Saithe   Blessed.

Salmon   A symbol of great wisdom, around which many legends revolve.

Seal   Often believed that seals were fallen angels. Many families are descended from seals, some of which had webbed hands or feet. Some seals were the children of sea-kings who had become enchanted (selkies).

Seelie-Court   The court of the Fairies, which travelled around their realm. They were usually fair to humans, doling out punishment that was morally sound, but they were quick to avenge insults to fairies.

Sgeulachd   Stories.

Selkie   Seals with the capacity to become humans, leaving their seal-skins to take human form.

Shi-en   Fairy dwelling.

Sluagh   The host of the dead, seen fighting in the sky and heard by mortals.

Somerled   Lord of the Isles, and legendary ancestor of the Clan MacDonald.

Stoorworm   A great water monster which frequented lochs. When it thrust its great body from the sea, it could engulf islands and whole ships. Its appearance prophesied devastation.

Thomas the Rhymer   Also called 'True Thomas', he was Thomas of Ercledoune, who lived in the thirteenth century. He met with the Queen of Elfland, and visited her country, given clothes and a tongue that can tell no lie. He was also given the gift of prophecy, and many of his predictions were proven true.

Unseelie Court   An unholy court which were a kind of fairy, antagonistic to humans. They took the form of a kind of Sluagh, and shot humans and animals with elf-shots.

✳   ✳   ✳

Further Reading

Ashe, Geoffrey, *Mythology of the British Isles* (1990) • Black, G.F., *Country Folk-Lore III*, Orkney and Shetland Islands (1903) • Bruford, Alan, and D.A. MacDonald, eds., *Scottish Traditional Tales* (1974) • Bruford, Alan, *Gaelic Folk-Tales and Mediaeval Romances* (1969) • Buchan, Peter, *Ancient Scottish Tales* (1908) • Chambers, Robert, *Popular Rhymes of Scotland* (1870) • Campbell, John Gregorson, *Clan Traditions and Popular Tales of the Western Highlands and Islands*, 1895 • Campbell, John Gregorson, *Superstitions of the Highlands and Islands of Scotland*, 1900 • Campbell, John Gregorson, *Witchcraft and Second Sight in the Highlands and Islands of Scotland*, 1902 • Douglas, Sheila, *The King of the Black Art and Other Folk Tales* (1987) • MacDougall, James, *Folk Tales and Fairy Lore* (1978) • MacInnes, Duncan, *Folk and Hero Tales* (1890) • Marwick, Earnest, *The Folklore of Orkney and Shetland* (1975) • Matthews, John and Caitlin, *An Encyclopaedia of Myth and Legend* (1995) • O'Sullivan, Sean, *The Folklore of Ireland* (1974) • Philip, Neil, *The Penguin Book of Scottish Folktales* (1995) • Robinson, Mairi, ed., *The Concise Scots Dictionary* (1985) • Thompson, Stith, *The Folktale* (1977) • Wilson, Barbara Ker, *Scottish Folk-Tales and Legends* (1954)

Notes on Illustrations

Page 3 A Midsummer Night's Dream, by Arthur Rackham. Courtesy of Fine Art Photographic Library Ltd. **Page 5** The Witches' Sabbath, by Francisco Jose de Goya Y Lucientes (Prado Madrid). Courtesy of The Bridgeman Art Library **Page 7** Rip Van Winkle, by Arthur Rackham. Courtesy of Fine Art Photographic Library Ltd. **Page 9** There is Sweet Music Here, by Charles Robinson. Courtesy of Angela Hone, Marlow & Fine Art Photographic Library Ltd. **Page 13** A Crofter's Cottage, by R.W.S. Myles Birket Foster. Courtesy of Fine Art Photographic Library Ltd. **Page 15** In Fond Memory, by Hans Thoma. Courtesy of Fine Art Photographic Library Ltd. **Page 19** Love Leading the Pilgrim, by Sir Edward Burne-Jones (Tate Gallery, London). Courtesy of The Bridgeman Art Library. **Page 21** The Invalid and the Birth, by William Van Strydonck (Musée des Beaux-Arts, Tournal). Courtesy of Giraudon & The Bridgeman Art Library. **Page 23** The Captive Robin, by John Fitzgerald. Courtesy of The Bridgeman Art Library **Page 27** Harvest Time, by George Cole (City of Bristol Museum & Art Gallery). Courtesy of The Bridgeman Art Library. **Page 29** The Flying Dutchman, by T.J. Dix (Sheengate Gallery). Courtesy of Fine Art Photographic Library Ltd. **Page 31** Salvaging a Wreck off the Coast, by John Wilson Carmichael. Courtesy of Fine Art Photographic Library Ltd. **Page 32** The Ferry near Inver, by Alexander Nasmyth. Courtesy of Fine Art Photographic Library Ltd. **Page 35** The Magic Circle, by John William Waterhouse (Christie's London). Courtesy of The Bridgeman Art Library. **Page 39** The Witches' Home, by Richard Doyle. Courtesy of The Board of Trustees of the V&A Museum. **Page 41** Dunderawe Castle, by Alexander Frazer. Courtesy of Fine Art Photographic Library Ltd. **Page 43** Ice Fishing, by Ludwig Munthe (Bonhams, London). Courtesy of The Bridgeman Art Library. **Page 47** The War in Heaven, by Gustav Dore's. Courtesy of Fine Art Photographic Library Ltd. **Page 51** Along the Dykes, by William Lee Hankey (Bradford City Art Gallery & Museums). Courtesy of The Bridgeman Art Library. **Page 52** The Bass Rock, by R.W.S. Myles Birket Foster. Courtesy of Fine Art Photographic Library Ltd. **Page 54** The Ploughman, by Harold R.I. Swanwick (Phillips, The International Fine Art Auctioneers). Courtesy of The Bridgeman Art Library. **Page 57** A Highland Fair, by Samuel Austin (Warrington Museum & Art Gallery, Lancashire). Courtesy of The Bridgeman Art Library. **Page 61** The Dance of the Little People, by William Holmes Sullivan. Courtesy of Gavin Graham Gallery, London & Fine Art Photographic Library Ltd. **Page 63** The Nixen Gun Brig, by Thomas Luny. Courtesy of Fine Art Photographic Library Ltd. **Page 64** The Bride of Lammermoor, by Sir John Everett Millais (City of Bristol Museum and Art Gallery). Courtesy of The Bridgeman Art Library **Page 67** The Dweller in the Innermost, by George Fredrick Watts (Tate Gallery, London). Courtesy of The Bridgeman Art Library. **Page 69** Missing, by Robert. F. Keem (Oldham Art Gallery, Lancashire). Courtesy of The Bridgeman Art Library. **Page 70** The Village Fiddler, by Adriaen Brouwer (Hermitage, St Petersburg). Courtesy of The Bridgeman Art Library **Page 73** Orphans, by Istvan Csok (Magyar Nemzeti Galeria, Budapest). Courtesy of The Bridgeman Art Library. **Page 75** Scottish Coastal Landscape, by John Glover (Phillips, The International Fine Art Auctioneers). Courtesy of The Bridgeman Art Library. **Page 76** Scottish Peasants Washing, by Thomas Miles Richardson. Courtesy of Fine Art Photographic Library Ltd. **Page 79** Clouds Passing Over Ben Moore, by Henry Bright (Oscar & Peter Johnson Ltd London). Courtesy of The Bridgeman Art Library. **Page 81** Castle Urquhart, by Charles Pettitt. Courtesy of Fine Art Photographic Library Ltd. **Page 83** Highland Hospitality, by John Frederick Lewis (Fine Art Society, Edinburgh).Courtesy of The Bridgeman Art Library. **Page 84** The Sheep Drover, by Octavius Thomas Clark (Strandberg Cove Gallery, London). Courtesy of The Bridgeman Art Library. **Page 87** Stobo Kirk, by James McIntosh Patrick (City of Edinburgh Museums and Art Galleries). Courtesy of The Bridgeman Art Library. **Page 89** Blake's Urizen, by William Blake. Courtesy of Fine Art Photographic Library Ltd. **Page 91** Linlithgow Castle, by Scottish School (Christopher Wood Gallery, London). Courtesy of The Bridgeman Art Library. **Page 95** Jack O' Lantern, by Arthur Hughes. Courtesy of Fine Art Photographic Library Ltd. **Page 97** Churchmill, Lundie, Angus, by James McIntosh Patrick (The Fine Art Society, London). Courtesy of The Bridgeman Art Library. **Page 99** Sorrow, by Helen Allingham (Atkinson Art Gallery, Southport, Lancashire). Courtesy of The Bridgeman Art Library. **Page 100** A Lark, by Archibald Thorburn (John Spink Fine Watercolours, London). Courtesy of The Bridgeman Art Library. **Page 103** A Secret Path, by Albert Durer Lucas. Courtesy of Fine Art Photographic Library Ltd & Haynes Fine Art. **Page 104** Highland Cottages, by Waller Hugh Paton. Courtesy of Fine Art Photographic Library Ltd. **Page 109** At Bay, by Sir Joseph Noel Paton (City of Edinburgh Museums and Art Galleries). Courtesy of The Bridgeman Art Library. **Page 111** Port after Stormy Seas, by Evelyn de Morgan (The De Morgan Foundation, London). Courtesy of The Bridgeman Art Library. **Page 113** The Sleeping Beauty, by Thomas Ralph Spence (Paisnel Gallery, London). Courtesy of Fine Art Photographic Library Ltd. **Page 115** Loch Colisk, by John Macwhirter (The Fine Art Society, London). Courtesy of The Bridgeman Art Library. **Page 117** Newark Castle, by Henry Pether. Courtesy of Fine Art Photographic Library Ltd. **Page 119** Highland Sport, by George W. Horlor (Malcolm Innes Gallery, London). Courtesy of The Bridgeman Art Library. **Page 123** The Chieftain's Candlestick, by John Pettie (Forbes Magazine Collection, New York). Courtesy of The Bridgeman Art Library. **Page 125** The Dog Gellext, by James Liston Byam Shaw. Courtesy of Fine Art Photographic Library Ltd.

Index